Introduction

About GCSE BITESIZE

- GCSE BITESIZE is a revision service designed to help you achieve success in your exams with **books, television programmes** and a website at **www.bbc.co.uk/education/revision**.

- It's called BITESIZE because it breaks revision into bitesize chunks to make it easier to learn.

How to use this book

- This book explains and tests the **100 things you must know** to succeed in GCSE science. It provides:
  - the key information you need in the 'Know the facts' sections
  - questions to test your understanding in the 'Test yourself' sections.

- Use this book to check your understanding of GCSE science. If you can prove to yourself that you're confident with these key ideas you'll know that you're on track with your learning.

- You can use this book to test yourself:
  - during your GCSE course
  - at the end of the course during revision.

- As you revise you can use *100 Things You Must Know* in several ways:
  - as a summary of the essential information on each of the 100 key topics to help you revise those areas
  - to check your revision progress: test yourself to see which topics you're confident with
  - as a way to keep track and plan your time: you can aim to check and test a set number of topics each time you revise, knowing how many you need to cover in total and how much time you've got.

- To help you, words that appear in **bold** type appear in the Glossary on page 90.

About GCSE

The National Curriculum for England and Wales sets four Programmes of Study and Attainment Targets for Science.

Sc1 Experimental and investigative science This is assessed by coursework which you will have to hand in to your teacher for marking. It is a chance to gain as many marks as possible even before you go into the exam. This book concentrates on ways in which you can improve your marks in the exams.

Sc2 Life processes and living things You might also know this attainment target as Biology.

Sc3 Materials and their properties You might know this as Chemistry.

Sc4 Physical processes This is also called Physics.

BBC

things you must know

WARWICKSHIRE
COUNTY LIBRARY

CONTROL No.

500

Science

Biology: Morton Jenkins, Chemistry: Rod Clough, Physics: Mary Whitehouse

DISCARDED

Published by BBC Educational Publishing, BBC White City, 201 Wood Lane, London W12 7TS

First published 2000

© Morton Jenkins, Rod Clough, Mary Whitehouse/BBC Worldwide (Educational Publishing), 2000

All rights reserved. No part of this publication may be rep form or by any means mechanical, electronic, recording or permission of the publisher.

Colour reproduction, printed and bound in England by Ebenezer Baylis

To place an order, please telephone Customer Services on 01937 541001 (Monday–Friday 0800–1800) or write to BBC Educational Publishing, PO Box 234, Wetherby, West Yorkshire LS23 7EU.

)site at http://www.bbc.co.uk/education

0122272737

Contents

GCSE exams

The examining groups all provide GCSE Science specifications (syllabuses) which cover the four attainment targets above. There is some variety in the precise details of these. You should find out from your teacher which specification (syllabus) you are following and obtain a copy of it.

Linear or modular?

Most GCSE science specifications are linear. This means that the exams at the end of the course, in June, test all your knowledge and understanding of the science you have learned in your GCSE course. You will have completed your coursework when you take the exams. There may be three papers, one each for Biology, Chemistry and Physics; or they may be integrated, with questions about all three subjects on each paper. Make sure you know what your papers will be like.

Other specifications are modular. If you are following a modular specification you will do short module tests during the course. The marks from these tests will contribute to the final mark for your GCSE. You will take one or two final exams at the end of the course. You need to check which topics will be in the final exam.

Single or Double Award?

Most students take Double Award Science. This means that, for your result, you will get a 'double grade' for science, DD or CC for instance. You need to know all the work in this book for Double Award Science. Some students spend less time on science and take the Single Award exam. If you are taking Single Award Science, check with your teacher which topics you need to know.

Foundation Tier or Higher Tier?

There are two tiers of examination in Science. Students taking the Double Award Foundation Tier exam can achieve grades between GG and CC. Students taking the Higher Tier papers can gain grades between EE and A*A*. Even if you do really well on the Foundation Tier papers you cannot gain a better grade than CC. If you do really badly on the Higher Tier papers and do not get enough marks for an EE you will be ungraded. This means you must make sure you are entered for the right tier. You should discuss with your teachers and parents which is the best tier to enter and when you get into the exam make sure you are given the right paper!

In this book the work that will only appear on Higher Tier papers is marked with **[H]**.

The exam papers

In the final exams you will write your answers on the question paper. The questions are usually in several parts. They often start with some information or a diagram. It is important that you read the information and look at the diagram to make sure that you know what the question is about. Underline any important words in the information – they will help you in your answers.

There's a space for you to write your answer and marks for each part of the question shown. The size of the space and the number of marks give you a clue to how long your answer should be.

For some questions you need to write more. There are often several marks for this work and you will be asked to write several sentences to explain your ideas. Make sure that you write good legible English with correct spelling. There are more questions like this on the Higher Tier papers.

Good Luck!

01 Cells

Know the facts

- A **cell** is the basic unit of structure of all living organisms, excluding viruses.
- All living cells have a mixture of chemicals called **cytoplasm** and a membrane, which controls the entry and exit of substances.
- Most living cells have a **nucleus**, which controls all the activities within the cell such as cell division. Exceptions include red blood cells in mammals.
- The main differences between plant cells and animal cells are that plant cells have a non-living cellulose cell wall surrounding the cell membrane and, when mature, have a large vacuole inside them containing cell sap.
- Many plant cells in leaves and stems also have **chloroplasts** for photosynthesis.

Test yourself

The diagrams show two types of cell.

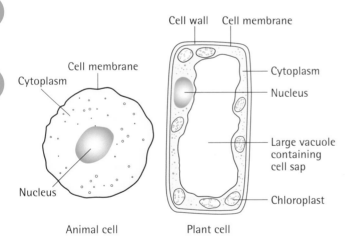

Animal cell   Plant cell

1 State the function of
   (a) the chloroplast
   (b) the nucleus
   (c) the cell membrane.
2 Name three structures, visible in the diagram, which only occur in plant cells.
3 Name a type of animal cell which does not have a nucleus.

02 Respiration

Know the facts

- **Respiration** is the process which releases energy from glucose in all living cells.
- **Aerobic respiration** takes place when oxygen is present. It is responsible for the complete breakdown of glucose, with the release of much more energy than when oxygen is not used.
- Water and carbon dioxide are the waste products:

   glucose + oxygen → carbon dioxide + water

- In **anaerobic respiration** in yeast, a little energy is released. Ethanol and carbon dioxide are the waste products.
- Some bacteria in milk respire anaerobically and make lactic acid. When we exercise vigorously, our muscle cells behave in a similar way.

Test yourself

Here is a very simplified diagram showing different forms of respiration.

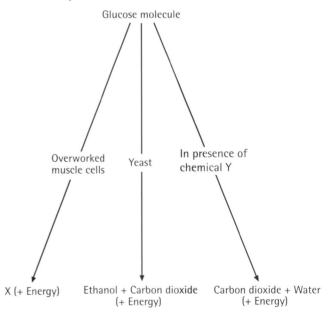

1 Name the product X.
2 Name the chemical represented by Y.
3 Name a commercial product which can be made by the respiration of yeast.

Know the facts

- **Enzymes** are **proteins** made by living organisms. They speed up the rate of chemical reactions, i.e. they are **catalysts**.
- They can be taken out of cells and used as extracts in products such as washing powders.
- They work only in a narrow range of temperatures and **pH** values.
- They are destroyed (denatured) when they are boiled.
- Each enzyme catalyses a particular reaction. Some help in building large molecules from small ones; others, like digestive enzymes, break large molecules into smaller ones.

Test yourself

1 Define an enzyme.

Hydrogen peroxide is a waste material produced in cells. It is poisonous and so is broken down into water and oxygen by an enzyme called catalase. Three different tissues were investigated as follows.

Three measuring cylinders were set up, each with 12cm³ of hydrogen peroxide and some washing up liquid. A 1cm³ piece of each tissue was placed in each of three measuring cylinders.

Bubbles of froth were formed and, at the end of three minutes, the volume of froth was recorded.

The apparatus and the results are shown in the diagram.

Look at the diagram and then answer these questions.

2 (a) Which type of tissue contained the most catalase?

   (b) Explain your answer.

3 State two other factors which must be kept constant to make it a 'fair test'.

4 What would happen if boiled liver was used instead?

5 Explain why it would be a good idea to repeat the experiment several times to calculate the average volume of froth for each tissue.

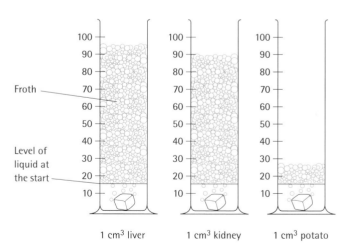

1 cm³ liver   1 cm³ kidney   1 cm³ potato

04 Diffusion and osmosis [H]

Know the facts 🐊

- **Diffusion** is due to the random movement of molecules. They move from a region of high concentration to a region of low concentration.
- **Osmosis** is a form of diffusion which involves only the movement of water molecules.
- **Osmosis** is the movement of water from where it is in high concentration to where it is in low concentration through a semi-permeable membrane until there is an even concentration of molecules.
- Cell membranes are semi-permeable.

Test yourself 🐊

The diagram shows a section through a root hair cell.

1 (a) State two differences between the terms diffusion and osmosis.
   (b) Explain why water passes from the soil solution into the root hair.
2 Suggest why most plants die if salt water is added to the soil in which they grow.
3 Describe another situation where osmosis takes place in living organisms.
4 Name a part of the body where diffusion of gases takes place.

05 Cell division [H]

Know the facts 🐊

- All **cells** are produced from pre-existing cells by cell division.
- Chromosomes in a nucleus are needed before cell division can take place.
- There are two main types of cell division: mitosis and meiosis.
- **Mitosis** produces two identical daughter cells from an original parent cell and is responsible for growth and repair of tissues.
- **Meiosis** occurs only in the production of reproductive cells. For every one cell that undergoes the process, four daughter cells with half the normal number of chromosomes are produced.
- Eggs and sperm are made by **meiosis**.

Test yourself 🐊

1 Name the type of cell division which is responsible for the production of
   (a) new skin cells when they are worn away
   (b) sperm.
2 If there are 46 chromosomes in a normal body cell, how many would there be in an egg?
3 Name a structure in a cell which must be present before cell division can take place.
4 The diagram shows a stage in mitosis.
   Name the structures A and B.

Know the facts

- **Digestion** is the breakdown of large insoluble molecules of food into smaller soluble molecules, by digestive **enzymes.**
- The digestive system consists of the alimentary canal and associated glands.
- The glands secrete digestive enzymes, breaking food down so that the nutrients can be absorbed into the blood system. **Carbohydrates** such as starch are broken down into simple sugars, **proteins** into amino acids, and fats into fatty acids and glycerol.
- Food that is not digested passes out of the body at the anus.

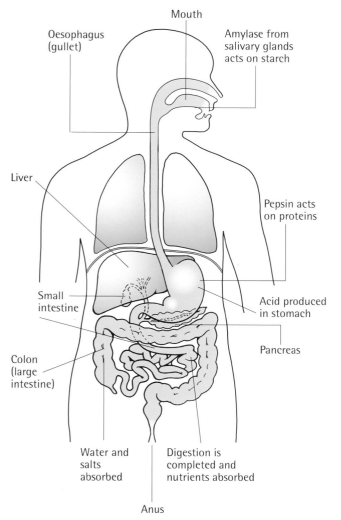

Mouth

Oesophagus (gullet)

Amylase from salivary glands acts on starch

Liver

Pepsin acts on proteins

Small intestine

Acid produced in stomach

Pancreas

Colon (large intestine)

Water and salts absorbed

Digestion is completed and nutrients absorbed

Anus

Test yourself

1 Bile emulsifies fats (turns them into small droplets). How will this help enzymes to digest fats?

2 State two things which need to happen to food before nutrients can be absorbed into the blood.

3 Name a place in the gut where
   (a) the contents are acidic
   (b) amylase digests starch
   (c) most water is absorbed from food.

4 Name an organ in the alimentary canal where the following enzymes work
   (a) pepsin
   (b) amylase.

5 Study the graph and answer the questions.

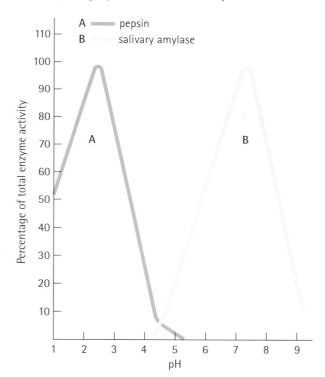

A ——— pepsin
B ——— salivary amylase

Percentage of total enzyme activity

pH

(a) At what pH is pepsin most active?

(b) Which enzyme has the widest range of activity?

(c) Explain why both enzymes cannot work together in the same place.

04

05

06

07 Absorption of food

Know the facts

- Absorption of food is the movement of molecules of digested food through the walls of the small intestine into the blood system. The nutrients can then be carried around the body to where they are needed.
- The lining of the small intestine is very thin and has its surface area increased by finger-like villi.
- Villi are rich in capillaries to absorb glucose and amino acids.
- They also have lacteals for the absorption of fat. The diagram shows a single villus

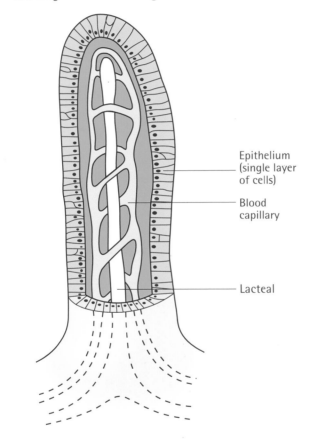

Epithelium (single layer of cells)

Blood capillary

Lacteal

Test yourself

1 In which part of the digestive system would you find villi?

2 How do the epithelium, blood capillary and lacteal in the diagram make the villus well adapted to its function?

08 Blood

Know the facts

- Blood consists of red cells, white cells and platelets suspended in a liquid called plasma.
- The red blood cells contain haemoglobin to carry oxygen to all parts of the body.
- The plasma carries carbon dioxide as sodium hydrogen carbonate from the cells to the lungs.
- The plasma also carries nutrients and hormones to the cells and urea as a waste product.
- Some white blood cells engulf and digest bacteria, while others make antibodies for immunity.
- Platelets help to clot the blood.

Test yourself

The diagram shows some of the structures and processes taking place in a blood capillary.

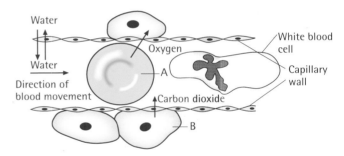

Water

Water

Direction of blood movement

Oxygen

A

Carbon dioxide

B

White blood cell

Capillary wall

1 Name the type of cell labelled A.

2 Which part of the blood carries
   (a) glucose
   (b) oxygen
   (c) carbon dioxide?

3 State two differences you can see between the structure of cell A and the structure of cell B.

4 Name one substance other than oxygen that passes from the blood to the tissues.

5 State one example of diffusion shown in the diagram.

6 Give two ways that the blood cells defend the body against disease-causing organisms.

Deoxygenated blood returning from head/arms

Aorta: the main **artery** which carries oxygen around the body

Pulmonary artery: takes blood containing little oxygen to the lungs

Arrows show the direction of the blood flow

Remember: diagrams of the heart are shown as if you are looking at someone else's chest, so the left side is on the right and vice versa.

Pulmonary **vein**: takes blood with oxygen back to the heart

Semi-lunar valve

Right atrium

Left atrium

Bicuspid valve: stops the blood going back

Tricuspid valve

Vena cava

Muscular right ventricle: squeezes blood along to the lungs

Muscular left ventricle: squeezes blood along aorta to body

Oxygenated blood to body

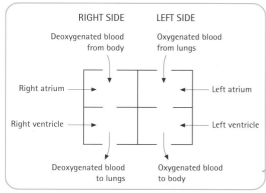

Simplified diagram of the chambers of the heart.

07

08

09

Know the facts

- In mammals the heart consists of four chambers (two upper atria and two lower ventricles) with the left and right sides totally separate.
- Deoxygenated blood is carried to the right atrium via the vena cava.
- Oxygenated blood from the lungs goes to the left atrium in the pulmonary vein.
- The blood passes into the ventricles through valves.
- The valves prevent back-flow when the ventricles contract.
- Contraction of the ventricles forces oxygenated blood around the body via the aorta and deoxygenated blood to the lungs via the pulmonary arteries.

Test yourself

1 Suggest why the wall of the left ventricle is more muscular than that of the right ventricle.

2 State the function of the valves between the atria and the ventricles.

3 The results shown in the table were the pulse rates of a student measured when sitting in a chair and after running up and down some stairs.

Activity	Pulse rate
	(beats per minute)
Sitting in a chair	70
After running up and down the stairs	130
2 minutes later	100
10 minutes later	70

(a) Explain the results.

(b) Suggest another factor which would have its rate affected as a result of this exercise.

(c) After the exercise the student's face looked red. Explain the advantage of this.

10 Breathing

Know the facts 📜

- Gas exchange in the lungs depends on movement of air in and out of the chest (thorax).
- During breathing in (**inhalation**) the rib cage moves upwards and outwards, while the diaphragm contracts, becoming flattened rather than dome shaped.
- Inhalation results in an increase in volume of the thorax with a decrease in pressure compared with atmospheric pressure so that air rushes into the lungs.
- During breathing out (**exhalation**), the rib cage moves downwards and inwards, the diaphragm relaxes and becomes dome shaped and the air is forced out due to an increase in pressure helped by the recoil of the elastic lungs.

Test yourself 📜

The diagrams show the position of the ribs and diaphragm during inhalation and exhalation.

Side view of chest (thorax)

A Inhalation (breathing in)   B Exhalation (breathing out)

 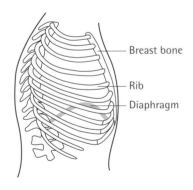

— Breast bone

— Rib
— Diaphragm

1 State two visible differences between the ribs and diaphragm in diagrams A and B.

2 Complete the following statements.

(a) During exhalation the volume of the thorax ...

> increases   decreases   stays the same

(b) During exhalation the pressure in the lungs ...

> increases   decreases   stays the same

11 Oxygen debt [H]

Know the facts 📜

- An **oxygen debt** occurs when a normally aerobic animal is forced to respire **anaerobically** during a temporary shortage of oxygen.
- If the demand for oxygen in muscle cells exceeds the supply, muscles respire anaerobically for a short time.
- This releases some energy but results in a build-up of lactic acid in the blood.
- This is particularly the case during 'burst' activities such as sprinting. At the end of the exercise the lactic acid needs to be broken down **aerobically** – the athlete breathes heavily to obtain the oxygen needed for this, which is called the oxygen debt.

Test yourself 📜

1 Name the type of respiration that does not need oxygen.

2 The table shows a comparison between two athletes who ran races of different distances.

Athlete	A	B
Distance of race (m)	100	10 000
Oxygen needed (dm^3)	10	150
Oxygen entering blood (dm^3)	0.5	134.0

The difference between the oxygen needed and the oxygen actually entering the blood during the race is called the oxygen debt.

(a) What is the oxygen debt for each of the athletes?

(b) When the race is over, both athletes continue to breathe more deeply than normal for some time. Explain the reason for this.

3 Write a word equation for the anaerobic respiration taking place in the muscles of an athlete with a large oxygen debt.

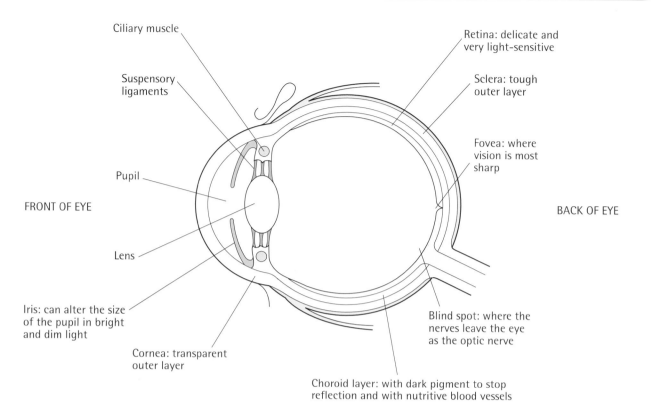

Ciliary muscle

Suspensory ligaments

Pupil

FRONT OF EYE

Lens

Iris: can alter the size of the pupil in bright and dim light

Cornea: transparent outer layer

Retina: delicate and very light-sensitive

Sclera: tough outer layer

Fovea: where vision is most sharp

BACK OF EYE

Blind spot: where the nerves leave the eye as the optic nerve

Choroid layer: with dark pigment to stop reflection and with nutritive blood vessels

Know the facts

- The vertebrate eye is a spherical organ connected to the brain by the optic nerve.
- It has an outer protective layer with a transparent front, called the **cornea**.
- The outer coat is lined with a black layer which supplies the eye with blood. Muscles are used for adjusting the shape of the lens and the **iris**.
- In the centre of the iris is a hole, the **pupil**.
- Light enters through the pupil, passes through the lens and reaches the light sensitive layer, called the **retina**. This contains receptor cells called rods and cones.
- Automatic focusing takes place during a process called accommodation.
- The eye focuses on near objects by contracting the ciliary muscles, slackening the suspensory ligament, making the lens more convex (fatter), and constricting the pupil.
- The eye focuses on distant objects by relaxing the ciliary muscles, stretching the suspensory ligament, making the lens less convex (thinner), and widening the pupil.

Test yourself

The diagram shows a human eye as seen from the front.

Iris (coloured part)

Pupil (black spot)

Sclerotic (white)

Sometimes the distance AB across the pupil changes.

1 Under what condition does the distance AB become smaller?
2 What is the advantage of being able to vary the size of the pupil?
3 The change in size of the pupil is a reflex action. Name one other reflex action performed by the eye and state its advantage.
4 Explain how the eye focuses on objects at different distances.

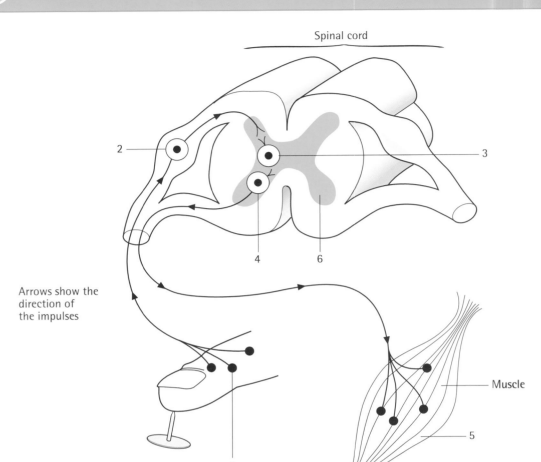

Spinal cord

2

3

4

6

Arrows show the direction of the impulses

Muscle

5

1

Know the facts

- A reflex action is an involuntary, rapid response to a stimulus performed when electrical nerve impulses are generated from a **receptor**.

- The impulses pass along a **sensory neurone** from the receptor to a connecting (relay) neurone in the spinal cord, then out via a **motor neurone** and eventually to the effector organ which brings about a response.

- **Effectors** are always muscles or glands.

- Examples of reflexes are sneezing, coughing, blinking and withdrawing your finger from a sharp object. Most reflexes protect the body in some way.

Test yourself

The diagram shows the path taken by a nervous impulse during a reflex action when a finger touches a drawing pin.

1 Choose six names from the following list to identify the numbers on the diagram.

effector	grey matter	motor neurone
relay neurone		sensory neurone
synapse	white matter	receptor

2 What are the advantages of a reflex action?

3 We are able to detect changes in our surroundings. What is the term used to describe these changes?

4 Name four organs found in the body which can detect a change in our surroundings and state the change to which each might respond.

Know the facts 📖

- **Insulin** is a **hormone** that controls the concentration of glucose in the blood.
- **Glucose** is maintained at a concentration of 0.1g per 100cm^3 of blood.
- Lack of insulin leads to diabetes (the inability to regulate blood sugar).
- Insulin is made by special cells in the pancreas.
- Its secretion into the blood stream is stimulated by high concentrations of glucose in the blood, such as are found after a meal.
- Insulin stimulates excess glucose to be changed into glycogen, which is stored in the liver and muscles.

Test yourself 📖

1 Explain the function of insulin.

Here are some facts concerning two types of diabetes.

> **Type 1:** This person produces little or no insulin. Daily injections of insulin are needed.
>
> **Type 2:** This person produces a lower than normal amount of insulin. Daily injections of insulin are not needed.

2 Suggest how a person suffering from Type 2 diabetes may control the disease.

3 The graph shows how the amount of insulin produced by untreated sufferers of each type of diabetes changes during a twelve-hour period.

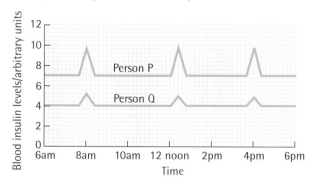

(a) Which person has type 2 diabetes?

(b) Suggest why the amounts of insulin increase in both graphs at certain times during the twelve-hour period.

Know the facts 📖

- Sex **hormones** cause the development of secondary sexual characteristics at the time of puberty.
- In females, the secondary sexual characteristics include menstruation, breast development, broadening hips and growth of pubic and armpit hair.
- In males, at puberty there is a deepening of the voice, increased growth of body hair and a general increase in muscle development.
- Certain cells in the ovaries and testes produce sex hormones.
- The ovaries secrete the female sex hormones, **oestrogen** and **progesterone**.
- Oestrogen promotes ripening of the egg and starts the thickening of the uterus lining.
- Progesterone maintains the growth of the lining of the uterus.
- The testes produce the male sex hormone called **testosterone**.

Test yourself 📖

1 State the name of the male sex hormone.

2 Where in the body is this hormone made?

The graph shows how the production of the male sex hormone is related to the age of males.

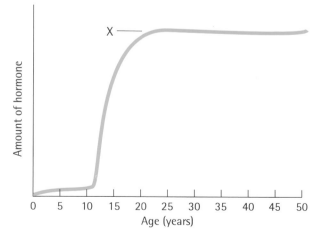

3 What is the term used to describe the changes to the body at point X on the graph?

4 List the expected effects of this sex hormone on the development of males between the ages of fifteen and twenty.

13

14

15

Know the facts ✍

- Each **kidney** has over one million tiny filters called **nephrons**.
- The kidneys control the chemical make-up of the blood by removing waste and regulating the blood's composition.
- There are two stages to removing waste from the blood: filtration and reabsorption.
- Filtration takes place in the tiny knot of blood capillaries, called a glomerulus, which sits in the cup-like Bowman's capsules at the beginning of each nephron.
- Filtration occurs because the pressure of the blood forces small molecules through into the tubule. These include water, salts, glucose and urea.
- Kidney tubules are parts of the nephrons that reabsorb useful materials.
- At the end of each nephron, the waste product – urine – contains some of these solutes, while others have been reabsorbed back into the blood.
- Urine passes from the kidney to the bladder.

The diagram shows one kidney tubule.

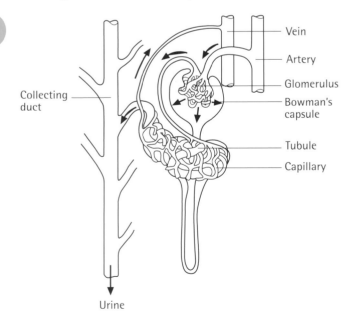

Collecting duct

Vein

Artery

Glomerulus

Bowman's capsule

Tubule

Capillary

Urine

Test yourself ✍

1 State the function of the capillary.
2 State what causes blood to be filtered in the glomerulus.
3 The table shows the composition of the liquid in the glomerulus and in the collecting duct.

Substance	Glomerulus (g per cm^3)	Collecting duct (g per cm^3)
water	90.0	95.0
protein	8.0	0
urea	0.03	2.0
glucose	0.10	0
salts	0.42	1.18

(a) Which substances have not passed into Y?
(b) Suggest what has happened to these materials.
(c) What can you deduce from the table about the functions of the kidneys?

4 Explain how filtration under pressure takes place in the Bowman's capsule (glomerulus).

17 · Kidneys and regulation [H]

Know the facts

- When blood is filtered through the walls of the blood capillaries in the kidney tubules, the filtrate contains some essential materials which the body cannot afford to lose.
- These include glucose, some mineral salts, amino acids and water.
- All of the glucose and amino acids are reabsorbed back into the blood capillaries which surround the tubules.
- Water and mineral salts which are needed by the body are also reabsorbed into the capillaries surrounding the tubules.
- The degree of water reabsorption is under the control of a hormone called anti-diuretic hormone (**ADH**).
- When there is little water in the blood, a lot of ADH and little urine is produced. When there is a lot of water in the blood, little ADH and a lot of urine is produced.

Test yourself

The composition of urine is regulated by the kidney tubules. The table shows information about the kidneys of three different mammals.

Mammal	Length of tubule (arbitrary units)	Concentration of urine
Beaver (lives in lakes)	1.3	dilute
Human	3.0	medium
Desert rat	10.4	very concentrated

1 How many times longer is the tubule of the desert rat compared with that of the beaver?

2 Explain how ADH controls the concentration of urine.

3 Why does a desert rat need to produce more concentrated urine than a beaver?

18 · Temperature regulation

Know the facts

Skin regulates your body temperature.

On cold days
- you shiver. The muscles under the skin contract and relax rapidly, thus generating heat.
- the blood capillaries in the skin constrict so that very little blood reaches the skin and so less heat is radiated away.
- the hairs on your skin stand up because the erector muscles contract. This traps a layer of insulating air between the hairs.

On hot days
- you sweat. The skin is cooled when the sweat **evaporates** from its surface.
- the blood vessels in your skin dilate so that more blood reaches the skin and excess heat is radiated from your body.

Test yourself

The diagram below shows some of the structures in human skin.

1 Name the parts labelled 1 to 3.

2 State what happens to the blood capillaries when the temperature outside is
   (a) very low
   (b) very high.

3 State another way in which skin reacts to a rise in temperature.

4 Why does evaporation of sweat cool the body?

19 Photosynthesis

Know the facts

- **Photosynthesis** is the series of chemical reactions in which **glucose** is made.
- In this process, light energy is converted to chemical energy and stored in glucose molecules.
- In the presence of **chlorophyll**, light provides the energy for carbon dioxide and water to undergo a series of **enzyme**-controlled reactions to make glucose and oxygen.
- The glucose is often rapidly changed into starch. The oxygen is used by organisms for respiration.
- Photosynthesis can be summarised as:

  carbon dioxide + water + light energy
  $\rightarrow$ glucose + oxygen

- The main factors which limit the rate of photosynthesis are the availability of carbon dioxide, light, and chlorophyll.
- As enzymes are involved, temperature can also be a limiting factor.
- Photosynthesis can be divided into two basic stages.
- Stage one uses energy from sunlight, which is trapped by chlorophyll and splits molecules of water into hydrogen and oxygen.
- Stage two uses hydrogen. This combines with carbon dioxide in a complex series of reactions. These reactions are the starting points for the manufacture of all carbohydrates, fats, proteins and some vitamins.
- Photosynthesis provides food and oxygen for animals. It also uses carbon dioxide from respiration to maintain a constant level of carbon dioxide in the atmosphere.

Test yourself

1 To test a leaf for starch it is **first** decolourised by being boiled in alcohol, washed in water and having a chemical added.
   (a) What is the chemical?
   (b) How will its colour change if starch is present?

2 List two advantages of having plants in an aquarium tank containing fish.

3 Give a definition of photosynthesis.

Two specimen tubes were set up as shown in the diagram. The water in the tubes was boiled to remove air before the plants were added.

Tube 1   Tube 2

Tube 1 was left in the dark and tube 2 was left in the light. After 48 hours the nail in tube 2 was rusty but the nail in tube 1 was not.

4 Explain why the process taking place in the plant in tube 2 caused the nail to go rusty (see topic 60 on page 46).

20 Transpiration

Know the facts

- The process by which water is lost from plants is called **transpiration**.
- Water evaporating from the leaves of a plant pulls up more water containing dissolved minerals from the soil.
- Much of the water is lost through tiny pores, called **stomata**, which occur on the surface of the leaves.
- Transpiration also helps to cool leaves by **evaporation**.
- The column of water is carried through the narrow xylem vessels which extend from the root through the stem to the leaves.
- The column is prevented from breaking up by strong attractive forces between the water molecules. This is called cohesion.

Test yourself

1 Name the structures in the leaf through which water is lost.

2 Name the process by which water is normally lost through the leaf.

3 An experiment to show water loss was carried out with three leaves of the same size. A waterproof layer of grease was put on the leaves as shown below:

> Leaf A: upper surface only
> Leaf B: lower surface only
> Leaf C: both surfaces.

The leaves were weighed and then hung in a warm room for eight hours. The results are shown in the table below.

Leaf	Mass at beginning (g)	Mass after 8 hours (g)
A	6	3
B	6	5.5
C	7	7

a) What was the loss in mass from each of the three leaves?

b) Through which surface did the greatest water loss occur?

21 Plant hormones

Know the facts

- Growth in plants is regulated by **hormones**.
- These are made in certain parts of the plant and are carried to other parts.
- Hormones influence the growth, division, and elongation of cells.
- The most widely studied plant hormones are called **auxins**.
- Different parts of the plant react differently to auxins.
- A high concentration of auxin seems to stimulate stem growth but inhibit the growth of roots.
- Auxins control growth movements in response to a directional stimulus, such as light from one side. The auxin builds up on the dark side of a stem, causing it to bend towards the light. This is called phototropism.
- Auxins can be used in selective weedkillers where broad-leaved weeds like dandelions are killed by high concentrations but grass is unharmed.

Test yourself

The following apparatus was used to investigate the effect of a one-sided stimulus of light on the direction of growth in plant stems.

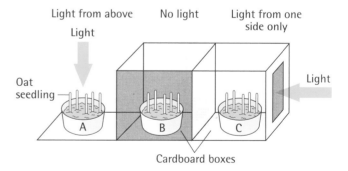

The plants were left as shown for three days and then the seedlings were examined.

1 Describe the expected appearance of the seedlings in A, B and C after three days.

2 Name one other directional stimulus that affects growth movements in plants and describe its effects on roots and stems.

3 What type of chemical is responsible for the growth responses in plants?

4 Why is phototropism beneficial to the plant?

Know the facts 🔖
- Natural selection is an evolutionary mechanism by which the total environment selects those forms that are best-suited to breed.
- Charles Darwin's theory of natural selection is based on three observations and two deductions.
- Observation 1: Organisms are capable of reproducing in geometric progression, that is: 2, 4, 8, 16 and so on.
- Observation 2: Numbers of a species tend to remain constant over long periods of time.
- Deduction 1: Most offspring do not survive to breed.
- Observation 3: All living things show variation.
- Deduction 2: By natural selection, those best adapted to their environment are more likely to survive to reproduce and pass on their **genes**. This is known as 'survival of the fittest', since they 'fit' their environment.

Test yourself 🔖
1 The **untrue** statement about natural selection is that it involves:
    (a) choice of a suitable habitat;
    (b) survival of the strongest;
    (c) selection of the best species by humans;
    (d) survival of the fittest to breed.

The Peppered moth exists as a light-coloured and a dark-coloured form. Both are eaten by birds. Before the *Clean Air Act* of 1956, both light and dark moths were released in two different areas and as many as possible were recaptured. One group was released near an industrial area where soot covered the trees. The other was released in a non-industrial area. The percentages of moths recaptured in the two areas are shown below.

Area	Percentage recaptured	
	Light-coloured type	Dark-coloured type
Non-industrial	12.5	6.3
Industrial	13.1	27.5

2 How do these data support the theory of natural selection?
3 Since the *Clean Air Act* of 1956, industrial areas have become much less polluted. Explain how this might have influenced the number of light-coloured moths surviving in these areas.

Know the facts 🔖
- **Mutations** are sudden genetic changes.
- There are two types of mutation.
- One type is a **gene**, or point, **mutation**. It arises when part of the genetic code in a **DNA** molecule is accidentally altered when the DNA is copied. Such a change alters or destroys a characteristic that is controlled by one or more genes.
- Less common than gene mutations are **chromosome** mutations. These may result in abnormal chromosome numbers when cells divide to form eggs or sperm.
- The frequency of mutations is increased by factors called mutagens. These include certain chemicals and radiation from radioactive elements.

Test yourself 🔖
1 The **untrue** statement about mutation is that:
    (a) all mutations are harmful;
    (b) mutation can be caused by atomic radiation;
    (c) mutation can be caused by certain chemicals;
    (d) mutations can be inherited.

In the 1950s there was widespread testing of nuclear weapons on islands in the Pacific Ocean. On one such island, before nuclear testing, there was much grass which was food for two forms of a species of snail. One form was striped yellow and black. The other was a rarer black form. Birds were the main predators of the snails.

2 Why do you think the black form was rarer?
3 The testing of nuclear weapons destroys vegetation and blackens rocks. What effect would you expect this to have on the numbers of the black form of the snail?
4 Many years after the testing of nuclear weapons on the island had finished, scientists visited the island and discovered a new brown form of the species. How might this have arisen?

24 Gender determination [H]

Know the facts 🐟📖

- The **chromosomes** that determine gender in most animals are called sex chromosomes.
- In mammals there are two types: the X chromosome and the Y chromosome.
- In human males they can be distinguished from the other chromosomes because the Y chromosome is shorter than the X chromosome with which it is paired.
- Males have one X and one Y chromosome.
- Females have two X chromosomes.
- Humans have twenty-two pairs of ordinary chromosomes and one pair of sex chromosomes.
- Some **genes** occur only on the X chromosomes and are said to be sex-linked.

Test yourself 🐟📖

1 The diagram below represents part of a living cell.

Name the structures labelled A and B.

2 (a) Copy the diagram below and write the correct sex chromosomes in the fertilised eggs, A and B.

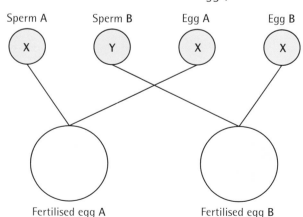

(b) State the gender of each of the fertilised eggs, A and B.

25 Genetic crosses [H]

Know the facts 🐟📖

- **Alleles** are alternative forms of a gene for a particular characteristic.
- The outward appearance of an organism is its phenotype and its genetic makeup is its genotype.

Steps in solving genetics problems
- Assign a symbol for each allele, usually a capital letter for a dominant allele and a lower case letter for a recessive allele. For example, T = allele for tallness, t = allele for shortness.
- Determine the genotype of each parent and indicate a mating. For example, Tt x tt.
- Determine all the possible types of sex cells each parent can produce. In this example, Tt → T and t, tt → t and t.
- Determine all the allele combinations that can result when the sex cells unite by drawing a diagram. In this example the possible allele combinations are Tt, Tt, tt and tt:

	T	t
t	Tt	tt
t	Tt	tt

- Determine the phenotypes. In this example, two tall and two short.

Test yourself 🐟📖

In koala bears, brown or white hair is controlled by a pair of alleles. B, for brown hair, is dominant to b, for white hair.

1 Name the structure in the nucleus of a cell where you would find the alleles.

2 (a) What is the genotype of a white koala bear?

(b) State the two possible genotypes of a brown koala bear.

3 A zoo keeper had a pair of brown koala bears. These were mated together and the offspring was white.

(a) What were the genotypes of the parents?

(b) What would be the chances of producing a white koala bear from a mating between a white koala and one of the parents in part (a)?

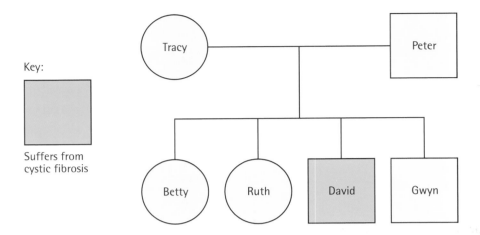

Key:

Suffers from
cystic fibrosis

Know the facts

- **Mutations** in **genes** may lead to genetic abnormalities which can be inherited.
- There are at least 4000 such abnormalities known in humans!
- The most common human **inherited disease** is cystic fibrosis.
- Cystic fibrosis is inherited as a recessive allele and leads to blockage of the respiratory bronchioles by mucus and also blockage of the tubes leading from the pancreas and liver. Sometimes disease-causing bacteria become trapped in the mucus in the lungs.
- Huntington's disease is another inherited disorder.
- Huntington's disease is caused by a dominant allele and does not show itself in people until they are in their late 30s. It results in the deterioration of the nervous system.
- Haemophilia is an inherited disease characterised by blood that does not clot.
- It affects men but women can carry the allele for the disease because it is recessive.
- The condition is an example of a sex-linked disease in humans because the gene is located on the X **chromosome** at a position that does not pair with the Y chromosome.
- If the dominant allele for normal blood clotting is carried on one X chromosome and the recessive allele for haemophilia is on its partner X chromosome in a female, she does not suffer from the disease.
- The male only has one X chromosome, so if that carries the recessive allele, he will suffer from the condition.

Test yourself

1 What is meant by the term 'inherited disease'?

2 Explain why sufferers of cystic fibrosis find breathing difficult.

3 Suggest why antibiotics help people who suffer from cystic fibrosis.

4 Tracy and Peter do not suffer from cystic fibrosis but one of their children, David, does suffer from it. The family pedigree is shown in the diagram.

Use the following letters in your answers:

N = normal (dominant) and n = cystic fibrosis (recessive).

(a) What is the genotype of

   (i)   Tracy

   (ii) Peter

   (iii) David?

(b) What are the two possibilities of Gwyn's genotype?

26

27

Know the facts

- **DNA** stands for deoxyribonucleic acid.
- **Genes** are made of a chemical called DNA which controls all living processes.
- It consists of a double helix, a structure like a ladder twisted into a spiral.
- The 'sides' of the ladder are each made up of alternating phosphate and deoxyribose sugar units.
- The 'rungs' are composed of pairs of what are called bases.
- Each base is joined to its partner by weak bonds.
- The partner bases are adenine (A) with thymine (T) and cytosine (C) with guanine (G).
- The order of the bases forms a 'code' for the production of proteins.
- Each gene is made of a DNA molecule with its own characteristic arrangement of bases.
- A change of just one base can (sometimes) alter a particular gene.
- There is an almost unlimited number of possible arrangements if you consider that a strand of DNA can be over 10 000 base units long.
- Therefore, there is an almost unlimited number of possible genes in all plants and animals.

Test yourself

1 (a) What is the name given to the shape of the DNA molecule?

(b) The diagram below shows part of a molecule of DNA. Using the same letters as in the diagram, give letters for the missing bases.

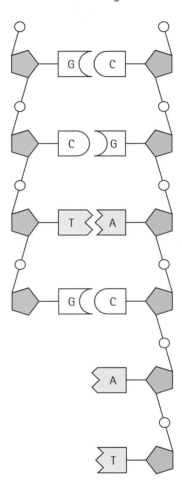

2 Genes are made of DNA which controls the production of proteins. One group of proteins in cells controls reactions by acting as catalysts. What are these proteins called?

Human DNA

Section coding for insulin

Stage 1

Bacterial DNA

Stage 2

Recombinant DNA

Stage 3

Know the facts

- The most common type of **genetic engineering** takes place by isolating a gene from one organism, using enzymes, and putting it into another.
- Scientists have isolated human genes that make **hormones** or blood proteins.
- They insert these genes into bacteria or yeasts. These microbes can make many identical copies of themselves by **cloning**.
- The process is rapid and relatively cheap.
- The human hormone can then be made by the **microbe** because the microbe now has the human gene in it.
- Large quantities of these valuable hormones can be harvested and used to treat various disorders.
- The process overcomes the need to extract hormones from dead animals.

Test yourself

Insulin is a hormone which is used to control diabetes. Insulin can be extracted from the pancreas of pigs and cattle but genetic engineering allows bacteria to produce human insulin. The diagram outlines the first stages in the preparation of human insulin from bacteria.

1 State what is happening at each of the labelled stages by matching the correct statement to the number of the stage.

(a) The DNA of the bacterium is cut.

(b) A gene is removed from a human cell.

(c) A human gene is inserted into the DNA of the bacterium.

2 Name the types of chemical which would be necessary at stages 1 and 2.

3 When bacteria have the recombinant DNA, as in stage 3, they undergo the process of cloning. What is meant by 'cloning'?

4 Suggest one reason why insulin produced in this way may be more acceptable to some people than insulin from pigs.

29 Food chains

Know the facts

- Green plants change energy from the sun's radiation into stored chemical energy.
- Much of this stored energy is released when plants are eaten.
- Some of it is stored in the bodies of **herbivores**.
- When a **carnivore** feeds on a herbivore, some energy is used and some is stored in the carnivore.
- A **food chain** traces the direction of energy flow through the various types of feeders, that is:

producer → herbivore → carnivore.

Test yourself

The table shows some of the animals which live in or near an oak tree.

Animal	Food
Bark beetle	Bark
Blackbird	Earthworms, beetles, caterpillars
Caterpillar	Leaves
Earthworm	Dead leaves
Hawk	Small birds
Mouse	Acorns
Owl	Mice
Squirrel	Acorns

1 From the data, name:
  (a) the producer
  (b) a herbivore
  (c) a carnivore.
2 Make a food chain with three links beginning with bark.
3 Explain the possible effect of a reduction in the owl population on
  (a) mice
  (b) squirrels.

30 Concentration through food chains

Know the facts

- One dangerous form of water pollution is that caused by industrial wastes containing heavy metals such as mercury, lead, zinc and cadmium.
- These heavy metals are by-products of mining and manufacturing processes.
- The concentration of heavy metals increases through **food chains** until those animals at the top of the chains are poisoned.
- Heavy metals interfere with the actions of many vital **enzymes** in animals and so cause death.
- Some insecticides, such as DDT, also increase in concentration from a harmless level at the beginning of the chain to toxic levels in top carnivores.

Test yourself

Look at the cartoon.

Have you been spraying your roses again?

Assume that the food chain in the pond is:

algae → small animals → larger animals → fish

Roses close to the pond were sprayed with an insecticide. Explain how this affected the fish in the pond.

31 Food webs

Know the facts 📜

- Inter-linked **food chains** are called **food webs**.
- Food webs give a more accurate picture of the feeding relationships within communities than food chains.
- For example, in an oak tree, there will be hundreds of different species which act as food, feeders or both.
- Even the most complex diagram of a food web will not be entirely accurate because many species eat almost any available food and some change their feeding habits during the course of their lives.
- For example, a caterpillar may feed exclusively on leaves but after it has changed into a butterfly, it becomes a nectar feeder.

Test yourself 📜

The diagram shows a food web in a forest.

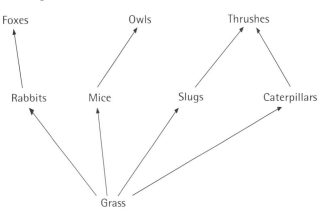

1 Why do all food chains begin with plants?
2 What is represented by the arrows?
3 If all the rabbits were killed by a disease, what two effects would this have upon other animals in the food web?

32 Food pyramids

Know the facts 📜

- **Food pyramids** show how much energy is available to organisms living in a measured area of land or a measured volume of water.
- There are three ways to represent these pyramids:
  1 A pyramid of numbers, which shows the number of organisms per unit area or volume in each feeding (trophic) level.
  2 A pyramid of biomass, which shows the mass of organic material per unit area or volume in each trophic level.
  3 A pyramid of energy, which shows the energy content at each trophic level, and the energy losses at each level.

Test yourself 📜

The biomass and names of some organisms in a lake are shown in the table below.

Organism	Biomass (kg)
Insects and leeches	500
Large fish	5
Plants	50 000
Small fish	50
Snails and worms	5000

1 Draw a pyramid of biomass using the information given in the table.
2 Which of the organisms are likely to be present in the least numbers?

33 The carbon cycle

Know the facts

- As a result of the **carbon cycle**, the concentration of carbon dioxide in the atmosphere should remain constant and there should be enough for plants to carry out **photosynthesis**.
- During **respiration** glucose, which contains carbon, is oxidised, releasing carbon dioxide into the environment.
- If there were no process to balance the effects of respiration, the carbon dioxide level in the atmosphere would increase and we would eventually run out of oxygen.
- When plants photosynthesise, they take in the carbon dioxide that would otherwise accumulate.
- The food made by plants enters food chains but eventually plants and animals die.
- The bacteria involved in decomposition return carbon dioxide to the atmosphere by their respiration.

Test yourself

The diagram shows the circulation of carbon in nature.

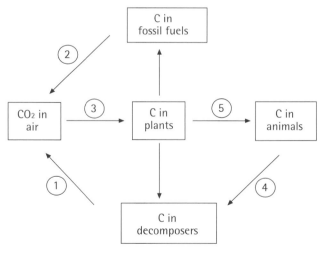

Match pathways 1 to 5 with the processes listed below.

burning of coal and oil

feeding

photosynthesis

respiration by microbes

decay

34 The nitrogen cycle [H]

Know the facts

- The **nitrogen cycle** helps to maintain a constant amount of nitrate in the soil.
- It relies on two groups of **microbes**:
  - those that break down large molecules containing nitrogen into smaller molecules
  - those that build up small molecules containing nitrogen into larger molecules.
- The microbes which break down large molecules are:
  - putrefying bacteria and fungi
  - denitrifying bacteria which break down nitrates into nitrogen.
- The microbes which build up larger molecules are:
  - nitrifying bacteria which make nitrates out of ammonium compounds
  - nitrogen-fixing bacteria which change nitrogen into compounds that can be absorbed by plants.

Test yourself

The diagram shows part of the nitrogen cycle.

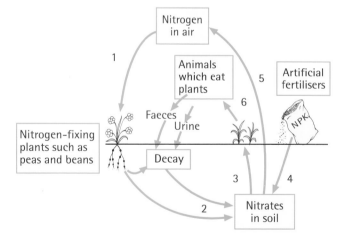

1 In what form do animals take in nitrogen by feeding?
2 State two types of microbe which are responsible for decay.
3 Which three numbers on the diagram represent places where microbes are involved in the nitrogen cycle?

35 Atomic structure

Know the facts

- **Atoms** consist of **electrons** circulating around a heavy **nucleus** of **protons** and **neutrons**.
- These sub-atomic particles have mass and **electrical charge**.

Name	Symbol	Relative mass	Relative charge
Proton	p	1	+1
Neutron	n	1	0
Electron	e	$\frac{1}{1840}$ (negligible)	−1

- The attraction between positive and negative holds the electrons around the nucleus.
- Atoms are neutral because
  number of protons = number of electrons.
- The number of protons is the **atomic number** (Z).
- Total number of protons + neutrons = **mass number** (A).

Isotopes

All atoms of an **element** have the same number of protons, that is, the same atomic number (Z), but they can have different numbers of neutrons, that is, different mass numbers (A).

Test yourself

1 Fill in the numbers missing from the table.

Atom	Sodium	Aluminium	Fluorine
Number of protons	11		9
Number of neutrons	12		
Number of electrons			
Atomic number		13	
Mass number		27	17

2 How many protons, neutrons and electrons does each of these contain?
   (a) $^{14}_{7}N$ (b) $^{11}_{5}B$ (c) $^{127}_{53}I$
   (d) $^{31}_{15}P$ (e) $^{56}_{26}Fe$

3 Explain why all atoms are electrically neutral.

4 Explain why the particles orbiting the nucleus do not fly away from it.

5 What does 'isotope' mean?

6 Oxygen has three isotopes: $^{16}_{8}O$, $^{17}_{8}O$ and $^{18}_{8}O$.
   Explain the similarities and differences between them.

36 Electrons in atoms

Know the facts

- Electrons orbit the nucleus in a series of **shells** or energy levels.
- Each energy level has a **maximum** number of electrons it can contain.
- The first shell holds up to two electrons. This is the lowest energy level.
- The second shell holds up to eight electrons.
- The third shell has two sub-levels. The first holds eight electrons and the second ten; eighteen in total.
- The fourth shell has three sub-levels. The first holds eight electrons, the second ten and the third fourteen; thirty-two in total.
- Energy levels are filled with electrons in order from the lowest energy level.
- The final arrangement of electrons is the **electronic configuration** of the atom.

For example: $^{24}_{12}Mg$ has twelve protons and thus twelve electrons. The electronic configuration will be 2.8.2. This is drawn as shown in the diagram.

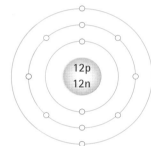

Test yourself

1 What is meant by 'electronic configuration'?

2 What is the electronic configuration of:
   (a) $_6C$ (b) $_8O$ (c) $_{17}Cl$ (d) $_{18}Ar$?

3 $^{23}_{11}Na$ is a sodium atom. For this atom state:
   (a) the atomic number
   (b) the mass number
   (c) the number of electrons
   (d) the number of neutrons
   (e) the electronic configuration.

4 Draw a sketch showing the complete atomic structure of $^{27}_{13}Al$.

5 What do $^{14}_{7}N$ and $^{31}_{15}P$ have in common?

6 The first two electrons in level 4 have a lower energy level than the second sub-level (of ten electrons) in level 3. What is the electronic configuration of:
   (a) $_{19}K$ (b) $_{20}Ca$ (c) $_{21}Sc$?

Know the facts

- The way that **elements** react depends upon the arrangement of electrons in their atoms.
- Only the electrons in the outer **shell** are involved. The nucleus and inner electrons do not change.
  Remember: Metal ions are positive, non-metal ions are negative.
- Atoms react to get a complete outer electron shell.
- All **compounds** involving metals are formed by ionic bonds.
- The metal atom loses its outermost electrons. It is now a **positive ion** because it has more protons than electrons.
- The non-metal gains these electrons into its outermost shell. It is now a **negative ion** because it has more electrons than protons.
- The attraction between these oppositely-charged ions is the bond that holds them together. It is called an **ionic bond**.

Example: The formation of sodium chloride from sodium and chlorine

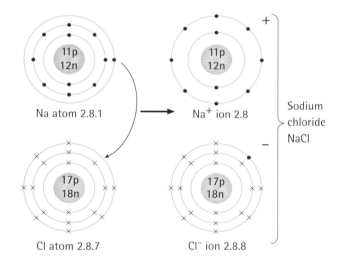

Na atom 2.8.1 → Na⁺ ion 2.8

Cl atom 2.8.7   Cl⁻ ion 2.8.8

Sodium chloride NaCl

- The number of positive or negative charges on an ion equals the number of electrons lost or gained.
- A sodium chloride crystal is a **giant lattice** made up of unipositive (one plus charge) Na^+ ions held to uninegative Cl^- ions by the attraction of positive for negative.
- All ionic compounds are giant lattices of this type.
- They are solids with a high melting point.

- They conduct electricity when melted or in solution in water.
- Some compounds are formed by the transfer of more than one electron.
- These compounds contain multi-charged ions. For example: the formation of magnesium oxide

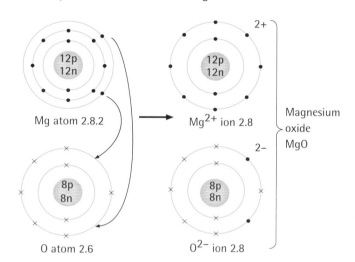

Mg atom 2.8.2 → Mg^{2+} ion 2.8

O atom 2.6 O^{2-} ion 2.8

Magnesium oxide MgO

Test yourself

1 What is an ion?

2 What is a unipositive ion?

You will need a periodic table for questions 3 and 4 (see topic 52 on page 41).

3 The sodium ion has the symbol Na^+. What is the symbol of the ions of
   (a) potassium
   (b) calcium
   (c) oxygen
   (d) magnesium
   (e) bromine?

4 Draw dot and cross diagrams to explain the formation of
   (a) lithium fluoride
   (b) calcium oxide
   (c) magnesium chloride.

5 State one similarity and one difference between
   (a) the magnesium ion and the sodium ion
   (b) the magnesium ion and the oxide ion.

Know the facts 📖

- When two non-metal atoms react together both need to gain electrons. They achieve this by sharing their outer electrons.
- Atoms are joined by shared pairs of electrons. One electron from each atom makes up the pair.
- The atoms are joined because the shared pair of electrons circulates around each of them. This is a **covalent bond**.

Example: The formation of methane (CH$_4$) from carbon and hydrogen

Each carbon atom has four outer electrons. Each hydrogen atom has one outer electron. Sharing gives both of them full **shells**.

- The atoms are bonded together into a molecule, which is separate from other molecules.
- Forces between molecules are low and easily overcome so the molecules are free to move around randomly.
- Compounds with covalent molecules have low melting and boiling points and do not conduct electricity.
- Sometimes covalent bonding produces **giant structures** by bonding atoms.
- These giant structures are hard solids with very high melting points.
- Examples are
  - diamond: carbon atoms covalently bonded into a continuous giant structure
  - sand: silicon and oxygen atoms in a covalent giant structure.

- Sometimes atoms are joined **by** two shared pairs of electrons and this is called a **double bond**.
- An example of this is the oxygen molecule, O$_2$.

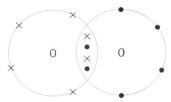

- In the nitrogen molecule, N$_2$, the bond is a triple bond.

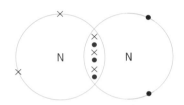

- This double- or triple-bond formation is necessary to complete the outer shells of **each** atom.

Test yourself 📖

1 What is a covalent bond?

2 What is a molecule?

3 Why do covalent compounds with simple molecules have low melting and boiling points?

4 Draw dot and cross diagrams to show the bonding in
   (a) water (H$_2$O)
   (b) ammonia (NH$_3$)
   (c) chlorine (Cl$_2$).

5 Why do giant structures have high melting points?

6 What is a double bond?

7 The compound ethene, C$_2$H$_4$, has a double bond between the two carbon atoms and single bonds between the carbon and hydrogen atoms as shown below.

Draw a dot and cross diagram to show the bonding in ethene.

39 Reactivity and the extraction of metals

Know the facts ✍

- The **reactivity series** is a list of metals arranged in order of reactivity, the most reactive at the top.
- Reactive metals are difficult to extract from ores whilst less reactive metals are extracted more easily.

	Metal	Extraction	
most reactive ↑	Potassium Sodium Calcium Magnesium Aluminium	By electrolysis (topic 41)	most difficult to extract ↓
	Zinc Iron Lead Copper Mercury	By reduction of the oxide (topic 40)	
least reactive	Silver Gold	Found naturally	easiest to extract

Displacement

- Metals can be displaced from compounds by more reactive metals e.g:

$$Zn\ (s) + CuSO_4\ (aq) \longrightarrow ZnSO_4\ (aq) + Cu\ (s)$$

- Whereas:

$$Al\ (s) + Na_2SO_4\ (aq) \xrightarrow{\quad\times\quad} \text{no reaction}$$

Test yourself ✍

1 What is the 'reactivity series'?

2 Name two metals more reactive than aluminium and two metals less reactive than iron.

3 For each of the following pairs write a word equation if you predict they will react and 'no reaction' if you predict otherwise.

(a) zinc and lead nitrate

(b) lead and copper sulphate

(c) zinc and magnesium chloride

(d) copper and silver nitrate.

4 Lithium is extracted from its ore by electrolysis. What does this tell you about lithium?

5 Explain why reactive metals are difficult to extract whilst unreactive ones are not.

40 Extraction by reduction

Know the facts ✍

- The rocks in the Earth's crust are mixtures of different minerals.
- It is from these rocks that we make many of the materials necessary to our life, such as glass, cement and other building materials, ceramics, acids, alkalis, hydrogen, chlorine and many more.
- Some of the rocks are composed mainly of the compounds of one metal and from these we obtain pure samples of that metal.
- Rocks from which we extract metals are called **ores**.
- The less reactive metals, zinc to copper in the reactivity series, are obtained by **reduction** of the oxide (see topic 61).

Examples

1 The main ore of zinc is zinc blende (mainly zinc sulphide). It is roasted in air to convert it to oxide. This is then reduced to zinc by roasting with coke (carbon).

$$2ZnS\ (s) + 3O_2\ (g) \longrightarrow 2ZnO\ (s) + 2SO_2\ (g)$$
$$2ZnO\ (s) + C\ (s) \longrightarrow 2Zn\ (s) + CO_2\ (g)$$

2 The main ore of iron is haematite (mainly iron (III) oxide). It is reduced to iron by carbon monoxide in a blast furnace.

$$Fe_2O_3\ (s) + 3CO\ (g) \longrightarrow 2Fe\ (s) + 3CO_2\ (g)$$

3 Metals such as mercury are so unreactive that their compounds split up on heating to leave the metal. This is called thermal decomposition (see topic 63).

$$2HgO\ (s) \xrightarrow{heat} 2Hg\ (l) + O_2\ (g)$$

Test yourself ✍

1 What is the definition of an ore?

2 Name four metals obtained from their ores by reduction of the oxide.

3 Name the main ore of zinc. Outline the extraction of zinc from this ore.

4 Mercury can be obtained by thermal decomposition of its oxide. Zinc cannot. Explain these facts.

5 Lead can be obtained from lead oxide by heating the lead oxide on a carbon block. Write a balanced chemical equation for this reaction and name all the materials.

Know the facts 📜💻

Sodium from sodium chloride

- Solid sodium chloride is made up of Na^+ and Cl^- ions held in a rigid lattice (see topic 37).
- Because the **ions** cannot move, solid sodium chloride cannot conduct electricity.
- When sodium chloride is melted the lattice breaks down and the ions are free to move.
- As a result, molten sodium chloride can conduct electricity.

Ions present:	$NaCl \longrightarrow Na^+ + Cl^-$
At anode (+):	Cl^- ions are attracted and lose electrons.
	$2Cl^- - 2e^- \longrightarrow Cl_2$ (g)
At cathode (–):	Na^+ ions are attracted and gain electrons.
	$2Na^+ + 2e^- \longrightarrow 2Na$ (s)
Overall:	$2NaCl$ (l) $\longrightarrow 2Na$ (s) $+ Cl_2$ (g)

Purification of copper

- Copper is extracted from its ore, copper pyrites (mainly copper (I) sulphide, Cu_2S), by heating the ore in air. This reduces it to copper.

$$Cu_2S \text{ (s)} + O_2 \text{ (g)} \longrightarrow 2Cu \text{ (s)} + SO_2 \text{ (g)}$$

- The copper is 98% pure and is called blister copper.
- Blister copper is purified by making it the anode of an electrolytic cell in which the cathode is pure copper and the **electrolyte** is an aqueous solution of copper sulphate.

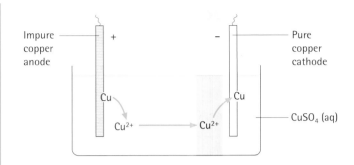

Ions present:	$CuSO_4 \longrightarrow Cu^{2+} + SO_4^{2-}$
At anode (+):	The Cu atoms of the anode each give up two electrons.
	$Cu \text{ (s)} \longrightarrow Cu^{2+} \text{ (aq)} + 2e^-$
At cathode (–):	The Cu^{2+} (aq) ions are attracted and each gain two electrons.
	$Cu^{2+} \text{ (aq)} + 2e^- \longrightarrow Cu \text{ (s)}$
Overall:	The **electrolysis** results in the copper dissolving from the anode and pure copper being deposited onto the cathode.

Test yourself 📜💻

1 Why does molten sodium chloride conduct electricity when solid sodium chloride is a non-conductor?

2 Give the name and symbol of each ion in sodium chloride.

3 Explain fully, with equations, what happens when molten sodium chloride is electrolysed.

4 What is blister copper? Outline how it is obtained from copper pyrites.

5 Explain fully, with equations, how blister copper is purified.

6 Using the examples above to help, explain fully, with equations, what happens when the following are electrolysed:

  (a) molten potassium chloride

  (b) molten aluminium oxide (Al_2O_3).

7 Sodium chloride melts at 800°C when the rigid lattice of Na^+ and Cl^- ions breaks down. Aluminium oxide melts at 2400°C. Suggest a possible explanation for the melting point of Al_2O_3 being about three times that of NaCl.

Know the facts

- All carbon atoms have four electrons in their outermost shell.
- This means they can form **covalent bonds** with four other atoms.
- For example, methane, CH_4:

- Carbon atoms are the only atoms that can join to themselves in chains, both short and long.

.... -C-C-C-C-C-C-C-C- .... etc.

- This means that the possible number of different carbon compounds is infinite.
- The study of carbon compounds is a branch of chemistry in itself. It is called organic chemistry.

Alkanes

- The simplest carbon compounds contain only hydrogen and carbon. They are called **hydrocarbons**.
- The simplest hydrocarbons are the group called alkanes.
- In alkanes all the bonds are single bonds and are directed to different atoms.
- Compounds containing only single bonds are **saturated compounds**.

Alkenes

- Another group of hydrocarbons is called alkenes.
- Alkenes contain at least one pair of carbon atoms joined by two shared pairs of electrons, i.e. double bonds.

- Compounds containing double bonds are **unsaturated compounds**.

Non-hydrocarbons

- Some classes of organic compounds contain other elements in addition to carbon and hydrogen.
- For example:
  - alcohols: contain the —OH group e.g. C_2H_5OH, ethanol
  - acids: contain the —COOH group e.g. $CH_3.COOH$, ethanoic acid
  - chlorides: contain —Cl e.g. C_2H_5Cl, chloroethane
  - amines: contain the —NH_2 group e.g. $C_2H_5NH_2$, ethylamine.

Test yourself

1 What is organic chemistry?

2 What is a hydrocarbon?

3 What property of carbon allows it to form more compounds than all the other elements put together?

4 Draw the structural formula of:
   (a) propane
   (b) methane
   (c) ethene
   (d) propene.

5 (a) What is a saturated compound?
   (b) What is an unsaturated compound?

6 Draw the structural formula of:
   (a) C_2H_5OH, ethanol
   (b) $C_2H_5NH_2$, ethylamine.

7 Suggest what might be the molecular formula of:
   (a) methanol
   (b) chloropropane
   (c) methylamine.

43 Fractional distillation

Know the facts 📜

- Crude oil is a **fossil fuel** formed over millions of years from plant and animal remains.
- It is a mixture of **hydrocarbons** with chains from one to hundreds of carbon atoms.
- These compounds have different boiling points and so can be separated by **fractional distillation.**

Temperature	Name of fraction	No. of C atoms in chain	Uses
about room temperature	gas	1–4	separated into simple alkanes and used as fuels
70°C	petrol	5–10	vehicle fuel
	paraffins	10–16	aviation fuel, heating fuel, manufacture of detergents
240°C	diesel	16–20	diesel fuel, manufacture of various chemicals
350°C	lubricating oils and waxes	20–60	fuels for power stations, ships, manufacture of waxes and greases
400–500°C	bitumen	60 plus	roads, roofing, waterproofing

- Most of the products are used as fuels because all hydrocarbons burn easily in air.
- For example:

$$C_3H_8 \text{ (g)} + 5O_2 \text{ (g)} \longrightarrow 3CO_2 \text{ (g)} + 4H_2O \text{ (g)} + \text{heat}$$
propane

Test yourself 📜

1 Why is crude oil described as a fossil fuel?

2 What is fractional distillation?

3 Name three of the fractions obtained from crude oil and for each fraction state:

(a) the approximate temperature at which it boils off

(b) the approximate length of its carbon chains

(c) its uses.

4 Write a balanced chemical equation for the burning in air of:

(a) methane (CH_4)　　(c) decane ($C_{10}H_{22}$)

(b) butane (C_4H_{10})

44 Polymerisation

Know the facts 📜

Cracking

- There is greater demand for short chain fractions of crude oil (such as petrol) than long chain ones (such as diesel).
- Heating long hydrocarbon molecules to high temperatures, usually with a catalyst, breaks them down into smaller molecules.
- For example:

$$C_{19}H_{40} \xrightarrow[\text{catalyst}]{\text{heat}} C_{10}H_{22} + C_4H_8 + C_3H_6 + C_2H_4$$

- **Cracking** also produces the unsaturated hydrocarbons called **alkenes** (see topic 42) which undergo **polymerisation**.

Polymerisation

- Double-bonded ethene molecules will, if heated under pressure and with a catalyst, **join** to form long chains of carbon atoms.

- The giant molecule produced is polythene (a **polymer**).
- The individual ethene molecules are monomers.
- Making polymers from monomers is polymerisation.
- Polythene, made by simply adding monomers together, is an addition polymer.

Test yourself 📜

1 What is cracking?

2 Why is cracking so useful?

3 Why can alkenes undergo polymerisation?

4 Explain polymerisation, giving an example.

Include an explanation of 'monomer' in your answer.

5 The structural formula of vinyl chloride is

Draw the structural formula of a section of a molecule of the polymer polyvinyl chloride (PVC).

45 Products from air

Know the facts

- Air is
  - 78% nitrogen
  - 21% oxygen
  - 1% other gases – the most important of which is carbon dioxide.
- Nitrogen from air is used to make ammonia, which is vital in the manufacture of fertilisers for agriculture.

The Haber process (see topic 68 on page 53)

- Nitrogen from air is combined with hydrogen (obtained from methane, $CH4$) to produce ammonia.

$$N_2 \text{ (g)} + 3H_2 \text{ (g)} \underset{\substack{500-550°C \\ Fe \text{ catalyst}}}{\overset{250 \text{ atmospheres}}{\rightleftharpoons}} 2NH_3 \text{ (g)} + heat$$

Manufacture of fertilisers

- The two most important nitrogenous fertilisers (i.e. nitrogen-containing fertilisers) are ammonium sulphate and ammonium nitrate.
- They are manufactured by reacting ammonia with dilute sulphuric acid or dilute nitric acid.

$$2NH_3 \text{ (g)} + H_2SO_4 \text{ (aq)} \rightarrow (NH_4)_2SO_4 \text{ (aq)}$$

$$NH_3 \text{ (g)} + HNO_3 \text{ (aq)} \rightarrow NH_4NO_3 \text{ (aq)}$$

Fertilisers and plants

- Nitrogen is an essential constituent of living matter. Nitrogen compounds, particularly proteins, are needed for healthy growth.
- Plants make **proteins** by taking nitrogen compounds from the soil and converting them to protein.
- Using the same soil continuously eventually uses up nutrients. They are replaced by adding fertilisers.
- Fertilisers produce high yields of healthy crops quickly.

Fertilisers and pollution

- Rain washes fertilisers into rivers and lakes. The fertilisers cause algae and bacteria to grow. These use oxygen and reduce light levels causing fish and plants to die.
- Rain washes fertilisers into reservoirs and hence into drinking water. It is thought that nitrates may affect the health of babies and old people.

Test yourself

1 Name the three main gases present in air.
2 State the percentages of the two most common gases in air.
3 What is manufactured in the Haber process?
4 Where does the nitrogen come from that is used in the Haber process?
5 State the conditions and write a balanced equation for the Haber process.
6 What is a 'nitrogenous' fertiliser?
7 Write balanced equations for the conversion of ammonia into two nitrogenous fertilisers.
8 Why do plants need nitrogen?
9 How do plants make the protein they need?
10 Why do farmers need to use fertilisers?
11 What effect do fertilisers have on crops?
12 Explain how fertilisers can cause fish to die.
13 Explain how harmful nitrates might get into drinking water.
14 The fertilisers described on the left are called 'artificial' fertilisers. Why do you think they are called 'artificial'?

Know the facts

The Earth first formed about 4500 million years ago. The table below indicates how the atmosphere may have evolved.

Number of years ago/ Process	Effect
4500 m • Earth forms • volcanoes begin to erupt	• atmosphere probably mainly hydrogen and helium • methane, carbon dioxide and water vapour are added to the atmosphere • the very light hydrogen and helium begin to drift off into space
3800 m • solid rocks form • water vapour condenses	• seas form • pure water at first but over time minerals from the Earth's crust dissolve in them
3500 m • first simple plant life appears	• plants begin to photosynthesise, taking CO_2 from the atmosphere and releasing oxygen • some of this oxygen dissolves in the sea
2500 m → 400m • animal life begins on land and atmosphere becomes as it is today	• animals use oxygen for respiration and so plants and animals begin to maintain a balance of carbon dioxide and oxygen in the atmosphere
present (and future?) • burning fossil fuels and clearing forests	• burning fossil fuels produces CO_2 • cutting down trees removes plants which use up CO_2 • hence the CO_2/O_2 balance is changing, with CO_2 increasing • this heavy gas remains in the atmosphere and traps heat (greenhouse effect)

Test yourself

1 Explain how oxygen was added to the atmosphere.

2 Explain how the level of oxygen might have changed over time and why it is now quite stable.

3 Outline how the seas may have evolved from reasonably pure condensed water vapour to their present state.

4 How does clearing forests add to the greenhouse effect?

5 Some scientists are worried about the effects of global warming. Outline some of these effects and explain why they might be a problem.

Know the facts

• Materials on the Earth and in the atmosphere are undergoing constant change but a balance must always be maintained.

• Nature achieves balance by recycling material.

• The most important natural cycles are the nitrogen and carbon cycles (see page 27) and the water and oxygen cycles.

• The carbon cycle keeps in balance the carbon dioxide level in the atmosphere.

• Carbon leaves the atmosphere by one route only: carbon dioxide being absorbed into plants by photosynthesis.

• Carbon returns to the atmosphere by three routes:
  – plants and animals releasing CO_2 during respiration
  – bacteria feeding on dead plants and animals and releasing CO_2
  – dead plants and animals becoming fossil fuels which release CO_2 when burned.

• The balance could easily be disturbed if there were fewer plants or more fuel was burnt (see topic 46).

• The diagram below summarises the carbon cycle.

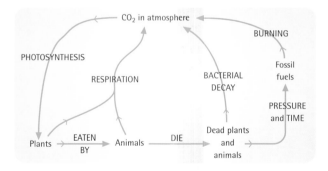

Test yourself

1 Why do we find cycles of material occurring in nature?

2 Name three of these cycles.

3 Explain how carbon from the atmosphere gets into the soil.

4 Explain two ways in which carbon is returned to the atmosphere.

5 How does the burning of fossil fuels affect the environment?

Know the facts

- There are three types of rock: **igneous**, **sedimentary** and **metamorphic**.

Igneous rocks

- When the Earth first formed it was probably molten.
- As it cooled, its outer later solidified to form the first rocks, which were igneous rocks.
- Igneous rocks are formed whenever molten rock (magma) cools and solidifies.
- Magma forms below the Earth's surface and rises.
- If the magma stops below the surface, it cools down slowly (over thousands or millions of years) to form rocks with large crystals (e.g. granite).
- If the magma rises to the surface it erupts from volcanoes. It can explode out of volcanoes as volcanic ash or flow out as lava. Lava cools quickly (in days or weeks) to form rocks with small crystals (e.g. basalt).

Remember:

rapid cooling ⟶ small crystals

slow cooling ⟶ large crystals

Sedimentary rocks

- Rocks on the Earth's surface are broken up by weathering and erosion to form sediments.
- Weathering breaks up and can dissolve the rock but does not move the fragments.
- Rocks can be weathered by freezing and thawing, heating and cooling, root growth or attack by chemicals in air, rain or soil.
- Erosion removes rock fragments, called sediment.
- The sediment falls off or is moved by wind, water (rivers or the sea) or even by animals, including humans.
- The sediment is then deposited in quieter conditions.
- Over millions of years layers of sediments can build up. The lower, older layers are compacted and cemented together into sedimentary rock (e.g. limestone).

Metamorphic rocks

- Metamorphic rocks are formed from other rocks by great pressure and heat but without melting.
- This happens deep below the Earth's surface when mountains are being formed.

- Slate is formed in this way.
- Cooling magma below the surface can also cause the baking and metamorphosis of nearby rocks.
- If the heat and pressure of mountain building is great enough, the rocks will melt to form magma that eventually becomes new igneous rock.
- Thus, over millions of years, rocks can be recycled in different ways.

Evidence

- Evidence for the processes by which rocks form and are recycled is not obtained directly. You cannot observe it happening because:
  - it takes too long
  - it happens too deep in the Earth's crust.
- The evidence is thus indirect and comes from:
  - studying how sediments are formed, how volcanoes erupt and the effects of earthquakes today
  - observing the features of rock in cliffs, quarries, mines and boreholes: sedimentary features, igneous features, and metamorphic features
  - study of shock waves travelling through the Earth after an earthquake (see page 68).

Test yourself

1 Explain why there was only one form of rock present when the Earth first formed.

2 (a) What type of rock are basalt and granite?

   (b) Explain how they were formed and the difference between them.

3 What is weathering?

4 What is erosion?

5 Describe the formation of sedimentary rock from igneous rock.

6 Outline three ways in which evidence for the ways in which rocks are formed and recycled can be collected.

7 Explain why fossils are found in sedimentary rocks. Would the fossils in different layers be similar or different? Explain your answer.

Know the facts

- All chemical reactions can be represented by
  - a word equation
  - a balanced chemical equation.

Example: The burning of magnesium

- The reactants are magnesium and oxygen and the product is magnesium oxide.
- The word equation is thus:

  magnesium + oxygen → magnesium oxide

- The word equation indicates what happens but tells you nothing about quantity.
- To get this information you need to translate the word equation into a balanced chemical equation.
- This translation is a two-step process:
  1. change the word equation into symbols and formulae

     so   magnesium + oxygen → magnesium oxide

     becomes Mg + O_2 → MgO

Remember:

- **elements** are written as symbols, so magnesium is Mg
- **gaseous elements** are diatomic, so oxygen is O_2
- **compounds** have a formula, so magnesium oxide is MgO.

  2. balance the symbol equation

     so $Mg + O_2 →$ MgO

     becomes $2Mg + O_2 → 2MgO$

Remember:

- balance one symbol at a time, reading left to right
- put balancing numbers only at the front of a formula
- when you have finished, go back to the beginning and check your equation.

Test yourself

1. Balance the following equations.
   (a) $Zn + HCl → ZnCl_2 + H_2$
   (b) $C + CO_2 → CO$
   (c) $H_2 + O_2 → H_2O$
   (d) $Al + Fe_2O_3 → Al_2O_3 + Fe$
   (e) $KOH + H_2SO_4 → K_2SO_4 + H_2O$
   (f) $ZnSO_4 + NaOH → Zn(OH)_2 + Na_2SO_4$
   (g) $Pb(NO_3)_2 → PbO + NO_2 + O_2$

2. Translate the following word equations into balanced chemical equations.
   (a) copper oxide + hydrogen → copper + water
   (b) sodium + water → sodium hydroxide + hydrogen
   (c) nitrogen + hydrogen → ammonia
   (d) zinc carbonate → zinc oxide + carbon dioxide
   (e) sodium hydroxide + magnesium chloride → magnesium hydroxide + sodium chloride

50 Reacting masses [H]

Know the facts

- A balanced chemical equation is quantitative and enables the masses of reactants and products to be calculated.

Example

Q What mass of magnesium oxide is produced by completely burning 6g of magnesium in oxygen?

(relative atomic masses: O = 16, Mg = 24)

A equation: $2Mg + O_2 \rightarrow 2MgO$

write in 2×24 $2 \times 16 \rightarrow 2 \times (24 + 16)$

atomic masses: 48   32 $\rightarrow$ 80

ignore the oxygen as you are not asked about it

divide by 48:   1 $\rightarrow \frac{80}{48}$

you have 6g of magnesium so

multiply by 6   6 $\rightarrow \frac{80}{48} \times 6$

therefore   6 $\rightarrow$ 10

10g of magnesium oxide is produced by completely burning 6g of magnesium.

Test yourself

Relative atomic masses: C = 12, Ca = 40, Cu = 64, H = 1, Na = 23, O = 16.

1 In the reaction

$CaCO_3 \xrightarrow{\text{heat}} CaO + CO_2$

what mass of calcium oxide is produced by the complete decomposition of 10g of calcium carbonate?

2 In the reaction

$2H_2 + O_2 \rightarrow 2H_2O$

what mass of oxygen is required to react completely with 1g of hydrogen and what mass of water is produced?

3 What weight of copper carbonate must be completely decomposed to produce 4g of copper oxide?

4 What mass of sodium must be burned completely to produce 0.62g of sodium oxide?

51 Determining formulae [H]

Know the facts

- Whenever a pure **compound** is made it always contains the same **elements** in the same fixed proportions by weight.
- This is the law of constant composition.
- This means that formulae can be calculated.

Example

Q In a carefully controlled experiment, 2.4g of magnesium was found to produce 4.0g of magnesium oxide. Calculate the formula of magnesium oxide.

(Relative atomic masses: Mg = 24, O = 16.)

A mass of magnesium oxide   4.0g

mass of magnesium   2.4g

hence mass of oxygen used   1.6g

equation: magnesium + oxygen $\rightarrow$ magnesium oxide

masses used: 2.4g   1.6g

moles used: $\frac{2.4}{24} = 0.1$ $\frac{1.6}{16} = 0.1$

Hence magnesium reacts with oxygen in the ration 1:1.

So the formula of magnesium oxide is MgO.

Test yourself

Relative atomic masses: C = 12, Cl = 35.5, Cu = 64, H = 1, Na = 23, O = 16, S = 32.

1 4g of hydrogen combine with 32g of oxygen to produce water. Calculate the formula of water.

2 2g of hydrogen combine with 32g of sulphur to produce hydrogen sulphide. Calculate the formula of hydrogen sulphide.

3 6g of carbon require 16g of oxygen for complete combustion to carbon dioxide. Calculate the formula of carbon dioxide.

4 4.6g of sodium burn completely in chlorine to produce 11.7g of sodium chloride. Calculate the formula of sodium chloride.

5 Reduction of 4g of copper oxide produces 3.2g of copper. Calculate the formula of copper oxide.

							O
			$_1$H Hydrogen 1				$_2$He Helium 2
I	**II**	**III**	**IV**	**V**	**VI**	**VII**	
$_3$Li Lithium 2.1	$_4$Be Beryllium 2.2	$_5$B Boron 2.3	$_6$C Carbon 2.4	$_7$N Nitrogen 2.5	$_8$O Oxygen 2.6	$_9$F Fluorine 2.7	$_{10}$Ne Neon 2.8
$_{11}$Na Sodium 2.8.1	$_{12}$Mg Magnesium 2.8.2	$_{13}$Al Aluminium 2.8.3	$_{14}$Si Silicon 2.8.4	$_{15}$P Phosphorus 2.8.5	$_{16}$S Sulphur 2.8.6	$_{17}$Cl Chlorine 2.8.7	$_{18}$Ar Argon 2.8.8
$_{19}$K Potassium 2.8.8.1	$_{20}$Ca Calcium 2.8.8.2						

The first twenty elements in the periodic table.

Know the facts

- The **periodic table** lists the **elements** in order of **atomic number**.
- The first twenty elements are arranged as shown above.
- Elements having the same number of electrons in their outer shell are in the same column.
- The vertical columns are **groups**. They contain elements having the same number of outer electrons and thus similar chemical properties.
- Horizontal rows are **periods**. Period 1 contains only hydrogen and helium, period 2 contains lithium to neon, period 3 sodium to argon and so on.
- Elements in a period have the same configuration of electrons in their inner shell(s).
- Following these first twenty the electrons begin to use the sub-level of the third shell (see topic 36 on page 28). This fills from eight to eighteen electrons over the next ten elements. These are the **transition metals** (see topic 59 on page 45). They fit between group II and group III.
- The complete periodic table is shown on the next page.

Test yourself

1 What is the periodic table?
2 What is a 'group' in the periodic table?
3 What do the elements in a **group** have in common?
4 What is a 'period' in the periodic table?
5 What do the elements in a **period** have in common?
6 What is a transition metal?

The complete periodic table

I	II			III	IV	V	VI	VII	O
									He Helium 2
Li Lithium 3	Be Beryllium 4			B Boron 5	C Carbon 6	N Nitrogen 7	O Oxygen 8	F Fluorine 9	Ne Neon 10
Na Sodium 11	Mg Magnesium 12			Al Aluminium 13	Si Silicon 14	P Phosphorus 15	S Sulphur 16	Cl Chlorine 17	Ar Argon 18

H Hydrogen 1

Na Sodium 11	Mg Magnesium 12

K Potassium 19	Ca Calcium 20	Sc Scandium 21	Ti Titanium 22	V Vanadium 23	Cr Chromium 24	Mn Manganese 25	Fe Iron 26	Co Cobalt 27	Ni Nickel 28	Cu Copper 29	Zn Zinc 30	Ga Gallium 31	Ge Germanium 32	As Arsenic 33	Se Selenium 34	Br Bromine 35	Kr Krypton 36
Rb Rubidium 37	Sr Strontium 38	Y Yttrium 39	Zr Zirconium 40	Nb Niobium 41	Mo Molybdenum 42	Tc Technetium 43	Ru Ruthenium 44	Rh Rhodium 45	Pd Palladium 46	Ag Silver 47	Cd Cadmium 48	In Indium 49	Sn Tin 50	Sb Antimony 51	Te Tellurium 52	I Iodine 53	Xe Xenon 54
Cs Caesium 55	Ba Barium 56	La Lanthanum 57 x	Hf Hafnium 72	Ta Tantalum 73	W Tungsten 74	Re Rhenium 75	Os Osmium 76	Ir Iridium 77	Pt Platinum 78	Au Gold 79	Hg Mercury 80	Tl Thallium 81	Pb Lead 82	Bi Bismuth 83	Po Polonium 84	At Astatine 85	Rn Radon 86
Fr Francium 87	Ra Radium 88	Ac Actinium 89 •															

This line divides the metals from the non-metals.

x Lanthanide series

Ce Cerium 58	Pr Praseodymium 59	Nd Neodymium 60	Pm Promethium 61	Sm Samarium 62	Eu Europium 63	Gd Gadolinium 64	Tb Terbium 65	Dy Dysprosium 66	Ho Holmium 67	Er Erbium 68	Tm Thulium 69	Yb Ytterbium 70	Lu Lutetium 71

• Actinide series

Th Thorium 90	Pa Protactinium 91	U Uranium 92	Np Neptunium 93	Pu Plutonium 94	Am Americium 95	Cm Curium 96	Bk Berkelium 97	Cf Californium 98	Es Einsteinium 99	Fm Fermium 100	Md Mendelevium 101	No Nobelium 102	Lr Lawrencium 103

KEY

X
element name

X = atomic symbol
z = atomic number

[1] Group I comprises the alkali metals. [2] Group II comprises the alkaline–earth metals. [3] Group VII comprises the halogens. [4] Group zero comprises the noble gases.

52

53 Properties of elements

Know the facts

- Group O contains the **noble gases** (see topic 54) which are chemically inert.
- From left to right across a period there is a gradual change from the most metallic elements in group I to the most non-metallic elements in group VII.
- Moving down a metal group there is a gradual increase in metallic properties.
- Moving up a non-metal group there is a gradual increase in non-metallic properties.
- Thus the most metallic elements are at the bottom left of the table and the most non-metallic are at the top right.

Test yourself

Refer to the periodic table in topic 52

1 Give the name and symbol of two elements you would expect to have similar chemical properties to each of the following:

   (a) sodium   (b) calcium

   (c) sulphur   (d) fluorine.

2 Where in the periodic table do you find

   (a) the most metallic element

   (b) the most non-metallic element

   (c) elements with atomic numbers 11–18

   (d) elements with six electrons in the outer shell?

3 The grid shows six elements in the periodic table. The letters are *not* the symbols of the elements.

I	II					III	IV	V	VI	VII	O
	A								B		
											C
D				E		F					

   (a) Give the letters of three metals and say which is the most metallic.

   (b) Give the letters of two non-metals and say which is the most non-metallic.

   (c) Write the formula of the compounds formed from

      (i) D and B   (ii) A and B.

   (d) What do E and F have in common?

   (e) Do D and A react together? Explain your answer.

54 Noble gases

Know the facts

- The **noble gases** are found in group O of the periodic table.

Name and symbol	Atomic number	Electronic configuration	Boiling point (°C)
Helium He	2	2	−269
Neon Ne	10	2.8	−246
Argon Ar	18	2.8.8	−186
Krypton Kr	36	2.8.18.8	−153
Xenon Xe	54	2.8.18.18.8	−108
Radon Rn	86	2.8.18.32.8	−62

- All have low boiling points, increasing down the group. This is because the atom gets heavier and so the inter-atomic forces are greater.
- All have electronic configurations with complete outer shells.
- These stable electronic structures mean that the noble gases are chemically inert.
- This inertness means that they are monatomic, that is, they exist as single atoms and not diatomic molecules like other gaseous elements.

Main uses of the noble gases

- Helium: less dense than air and does not burn, therefore used to fill airships and weather balloons.
- Neon: glows brightly when electricity is passed through it, therefore used in advertising signs.
- Argon: used to fill domestic light bulbs because its inertness prevents the filament from burning away.

Test yourself

1 Why do the boiling points of the noble gases increase down the group?

2 Why are the noble gases sometimes called the 'inert gases'?

3 Explain what is meant by 'monatomic' and why the noble gases are monatomic.

4 Explain why helium is used in weather balloons.

5 Why is argon used to fill domestic light bulbs?

53
54
55
56

55 Alkali metals

Know the facts

• The **alkali metals** are group 1 of the periodic table.

Name and symbol	Atomic number	Electronic configuration	Melting point (°C)
Lithium Li	3	2.1	180
Sodium Na	11	2.8.1	98
Potassium K	19	2.8.8.1	63.5
Rubidium Rb	37	2.8.18.8.1	39
Caesium Cs	55	2.8.18.18.8.1	29
Francium Fr	87	2.8.18.32.8.1	?

• All have low melting points, decreasing down the group because the structure of the larger atoms is easier to disrupt with heat.

• **Reactivity** increases down the group as the one outer electron, which is lost during a reaction to form the M^+ ion, is more easily lost. This is because it is further from the positive nucleus and thus less firmly held.

• The alkali metals react with:

1 oxygen, when burnt in air, to form oxides
$$4M (s) + O_2 (g) \rightarrow 2M_2O (s)$$

2 water, to form hydrogen plus an alkaline solution of the hydroxide
$$2M (s) + 2H_2O (l) \rightarrow 2MOH (aq) + H_2 (g)$$

3 the group VII **halogens**, to form halides
$$2M (s) + X_2 (g) \rightarrow 2MX (s)$$

Test yourself

1 Why are the chemical reactions of the alkali metals the same throughout the group?

2 Why does reactivity increase with increasing atomic number?

3 Write the formula of the reactions between:
   (a) the chloride of potassium
   (b) the oxide of sodium
   (c) the hydroxide of lithium.

4 Write balanced equations and name the products for:
   (a) sodium and bromine
   (b) potassium and oxygen
   (c) sodium and water.

56 Alkali metal compounds

Know the facts

• All alkali metal compounds are soluble in water.

• Because the alkali metals are reactive their compounds are stable and are not decomposed by heat.

• However, when molten they can be decomposed by electricity, e.g.
$$2NaCl (l) \xrightarrow{electrolysis} 2Na (s) + Cl_2 (g)$$

[H]

• All alkali metal compounds are **ionic**.

• For example: $NaOH \rightarrow Na^+ + OH^-$

Some uses of sodium compounds

Compound	Uses
Sodium chloride	• electrolysed in solution to produce NaOH, H_2 and Cl_2 • in the manufacture of sodium carbonate (washing soda) • in food as a preservative
Sodium carbonate (washing soda)	• in the manufacture of glass • to soften hard water
Sodium hydroxide (caustic soda)	• in the manufacture of soaps and detergents • in paper making • in the manufacture of ceramics

Test yourself

1 What happens, if anything, when sodium carbonate is heated? Explain your answer.

2 Explain how potassium could be extracted from potassium chloride.

3 Which sodium compound can be used in the production of:
   (a) glass   (b) soap
   (c) paper   (d) hydrogen
   (e) chlorine   (f) ceramics
   (g) sodium hydroxide   (h) washing soda

[H]

4 Which ions make up each of the following:
   (a) K_2O (b) LiOH
   (c) Na_2CO_3 (d) potassium sulphate
   (e) sodium nitrate   (f) potassium bromide

53

54

55

56

Know the facts

- The **halogens** are group VII of the periodic table.

Name and symbol	Atomic number	Electronic configuration	Colour and physical state at room temp	Boiling point (°C)
Fluorine F	9	2.7	pale yellow gas	−188
Chlorine Cl	17	2.8.7	green-yellow gas	−35
Bromine Br	35	2.8.18.7	dark red liquid	59
Iodine I	53	2.8.18.18.7	shiny purple solid	185
Astatine At	85	2.8.18.32.18.7	?	?

- All are coloured, getting darker down the group.
- All have low melting and boiling points, increasing down the group.
- All are diatomic molecules X_2. The two atoms are joined by a **covalent bond**.
- **Reactivity** decreases down the group. This is because the one outer electron gained during reaction, to form the X^- ion, is gained more quickly the nearer the outer shell is to the positive nucleus.
- The halogens react with:
  1. the alkali metals to form halides
     $$M\ (s) + X_2\ (g) \rightarrow 2MX\ (s)$$
  2. hydrogen to form hydrogen halides
     $$H_2\ (g) + X_2\ (g) \rightarrow 2HX\ (g)$$
- The hydrogen halides dissolve in water to form acids (see topic 62).

Test yourself

1 Predict for astatine
  (a) its colour
  (b) its physical state at room temperature
  (c) its boiling point.
2 Write balanced chemical equations and name the products for each of the following reactions.
  (a) sodium and iodine
  (b) bromine and hydrogen
3 Outline how chlorine is made into hydrochloric acid. Give equations where appropriate.
4 The melting point of chlorine is −101°C and of bromine is −7°C. Predict the melting points of iodine and astatine.

Know the facts

Displacement
- A more reactive halogen will **displace** a less reactive halogen from a solution of the ionic compound of the less reactive halogen.
- Chlorine displaces bromine from potassium bromide solution.
  $$Cl_2\ (g) + 2KBr\ (aq) \rightarrow Br_2\ (l) + 2KCl\ (aq)$$
- Bromine displaces iodine from potassium iodide solution.
  $$Br_2\ (l) + 2KI\ (aq) \rightarrow I_2\ (s) + 2KBr\ (aq)$$
- These reactions can be seen as similar to the reactivity series of metals in which the more reactive metal displaces the less reactive (see topic 39 on page 31).

[H]
Bonding in halogen compounds
- The halogens form **ionic** compounds with metals.
  $$MX \rightarrow M^+ + X^-$$
  $$MX_2 \rightarrow M^{2+} + 2X^-$$
- They also form **covalent** molecules with other non-metals. For example,

HCl, hydrogen chloride and Cl_2O, chlorine oxide

 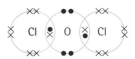

Test yourself

1 Write a balanced chemical equation or write 'no reaction' for each of the following pairs of reactants.
  (a) chlorine and sodium bromide
  (b) iodine and sodium chloride
  (c) bromine and sodium iodide
  (d) iodine and sodium bromide

[H]
2 Which ions make up each of the following?
  (a) calcium chloride   (b) sodium iodide
  (c) magnesium bromide   (d) lithium chloride
3 Draw dot and cross diagrams to show the covalent bonding in each of the following.
  (a) hydrogen bromide   (b) diatomic bromine
  (c) phosphorus trichloride (d) chloric (I) acid
      (PCl_3) (HOCl)

Know the facts

- The **transition metals** are found in the periodic table in the block between group II and group III.
- The elements in the first transition series are shown in the table.

Name and symbol	Atomic number	Electronic configuration	Melting point (°C)
Scandium Sc	21	2.8.9.2	1540
Titanium Ti	22	2.8.10.2	1670
Vanadium V	23	2.8.11.2	1800
Chromium Cr	24	2.8.12.2	1850
Manganese Mn	25	2.8.13.2	1245
Iron Fe	26	2.8.14.2	1530
Cobalt Co	27	2.8.15.2	1490
Nickel Ni	28	2.8.16.2	1450
Copper Cu	29	2.8.17.2	1083
Zinc Zn	30	2.8.18.2	420

- These metals are good **conductors** of electricity because the spaces in the incomplete shell allow electron movement.
- They have strong inter-atomic forces and this results in high melting points.
- They have similar-sized atoms because the number of electron shells in use is the same across the series.
- Because of their similar electronic configurations there are considerable similarities across the series. This means you do not see the trends you see moving down the group in the alkali metals, the halogens and the noble gases.
- Unlike the metals in groups I and II, which all have white compounds forming colourless aqueous solutions, the transition metals have coloured compounds forming coloured solutions, for example, blue copper sulphate, green nickel sulphate.
- Zinc is included in the series but its inner electron shells are completely filled. It therefore has white compounds which form colourless solutions.

[H]
- Metals in the first transition series lose electrons to form positive ions in reaction.

$$M - 2e^- \rightarrow M^{2+}$$

- Many of them demonstrate variable electron loss depending upon the reaction and conditions.

$$Fe - 2e^- \rightarrow Fe^{2+} \quad \text{or} \quad Fe - 3e^- \rightarrow Fe^{3+}$$

Properties and uses of transition metals

Metal	Properties	Uses
Titanium	• great strength • resistant to corrosion • light	• in aircraft • in replacement hip joints
Chromium	• extremely hard • resistant to corrosion	• used in steel alloys • plating
Iron	• not particularly hard • quite reactive	• used in steel, cast iron and wrought iron • as a catalyst in processes such as the Haber process
Copper	• malleable • ductile • resistant to corrosion • excellent conductor of heat and electricity	• used in wiring, piping, containers, etc.
Zinc	• highly resistant to corrosion • zinc is more reactive than iron so the protection continues even if the iron is exposed	• used to protect iron articles by coating (galvanising)

Test yourself

1 Explain why the transition metals
   (a) are good conductors of electricity
   (b) have high melting points
   (c) have similar-sized atoms
   (d) have similar physical and chemical properties
   (e) are all metals.
2 Explain why compounds of zinc are white whilst compounds of other transition metals are coloured.
3 Tin is less reactive than iron. Explain why tin plating of iron is not as effective a protection as galvanising.
4 Explain why zinc has a low melting point compared to the other metals in the series.

60 Oxidation

Know the facts

- Both gain of oxygen and loss of hydrogen in a chemical reaction are called **oxidation**.

Gain of oxygen in a chemical reaction
- For example:

$$H_2 (g) + CuO (s) \longrightarrow H_2O (g) + Cu (s)$$
oxidation

- The provider of oxygen is the oxidising agent. This is CuO in the example.
- **Combustion** (burning) is oxidation.

$$2Mg (s) + O_2 (g) \longrightarrow 2MgO (s)$$
oxidation

- The oxygen is the oxidising agent in this example.

Loss of hydrogen in a chemical reaction
- For example:

$$H_2S (g) + Cl_2 (g) \longrightarrow 2HCl (g) + S (s)$$
oxidation

- The H_2S is oxidised to S by loss of hydrogen.
- The hydrogen is removed by chlorine and so chlorine is the oxidising agent.

Oxidation involving electrons
[H]
- An atom is said to be oxidised when it loses electrons in a chemical reaction.
- For example:

$$Zn (s) + 2HCl (aq) \rightarrow ZnCl_2 (aq) + H_2 (g)$$

- Each zinc atom loses two electrons in the course of the reaction.
- The electrons go to the two hydrogen ions in the 2HCl.
- The zinc atoms are oxidised by electron loss.
- This is written as:

$$Zn - 2e^- \longrightarrow Zn^{2+} \quad or \quad Zn \longrightarrow Zn^{2+} - 2e^-$$
oxidation   oxidation

- The hydrogen ions, the takers of the electrons, are the oxidising agent.

- This explanation can also be **applied** to the burning of magnesium.

$$2Mg (s) + O_2 (g) \rightarrow 2MgO (s)$$

- During the reaction, each Mg atom loses two electrons and is oxidised.

$$Mg - 2e^- \longrightarrow Mg^{2+}$$
oxidation

- The electrons go to the O_2 to make it into O^{2-}; thus the O_2 is the oxidising agent.

Test yourself

1 Define oxidation in terms of both oxygen and hydrogen.

2 Explain, in terms of both oxygen and hydrogen, what an oxidising agent is.

3 In each of the following, say which material is oxidised and which material is the oxidising agent.
   (a) $ZnO (s) + C (s) \rightarrow ZnO (s) + CO (g)$
   (b) $Fe_2O_3 + 3CO (g) \rightarrow 2Fe (s) + 3CO_2 (g)$
   (c) $S (s) + O_2 (g) \rightarrow SO_2 (g)$
   (d) $Cl_2 (g) + 2HBr (aq) \rightarrow 2HCl (aq) + Br_2 (l)$
   (e) $CH_4 (g) + 2Cl_2 (g) \rightarrow C (s) + 4HCl (g)$

[H]
4 In each of the following, explain why the first reactant can be said to have been oxidised.
   (a) $4Na (s) + O_2 (g) \rightarrow 2Na_2O (s)$
   (b) $Ca (s) + 2H_2O (l) \rightarrow Ca(OH)_2 (aq) + H_2 (g)$
   (c) $2Na (s) + Cl_2 (g) \rightarrow 2NaCl (s)$
   (d) $Fe (s) + CuSO_4 (aq) \rightarrow FeSO_4 (aq) + Cu (s)$

   In each case write an equation involving electrons in your explanation.

61 Reduction and redox reactions

Know the facts

- **Reduction** is the opposite of **oxidation** and is therefore:
  1. loss of oxygen in a chemical reaction
  2. gain of hydrogen in a chemical reaction
  3. gain of electrons in a chemical reaction.

Loss of oxygen in a chemical reaction

- For example:

$$PbO\ (s) + C\ (s) \longrightarrow Pb\ (s) + CO\ (g)$$
reduction

- PbO is reduced to Pb by oxygen loss. C is the reducing agent.

Gain of hydrogen in a chemical reaction

- For example:

$$Cl_2\ (g) + 2HI\ (aq) \longrightarrow 2HCl\ (aq) + I_2\ (s)$$
reduction

- Cl_2 is reduced to HCl by hydrogen gain. HI is the reducing agent.

Gain of electrons in a chemical reaction

- For example:

$$2K\ (s) + Cl_2\ (g) \rightarrow 2KCl\ (s)$$

- Each Cl atom gains an electron to become a Cl^- ion:

$$Cl + e^- \rightarrow Cl^-.$$

- Cl_2 is reduced by electron gain. K is the reducing agent.

[H]
Redox reactions

- Oxidation and reduction always occur together in a reaction.
- These reactions are called **redox reactions**.
- For example:

1. oxidation (oxygen gain)

oxidising agent
$$PbO\ (s) \quad + \quad C\ (s) \longrightarrow Pb\ (s) \quad + \quad CO\ (g)$$
reducing agent

reduction (oxygen loss)

2. reduction (hydrogen gain)

reducing agent
$$H_2S\ (g) \quad + \quad Cl_2\ (g) \longrightarrow S\ (s) \quad + \quad 2HCl\ (g)$$
oxidising agent

oxidation (hydrogen loss)

- In redox reactions, the oxidising agent is reduced and the reducing agent is oxidised. For example:

$$2Mg\ (s) + O_2\ (g) \rightarrow 2MgO\ (s)$$

- The two electrons lost by each Mg atom are gained by each O atom.

$$2Mg - 4e^- \rightarrow 2Mg^{2+} \quad = \quad \text{oxidation}$$
$$O_2 + 4e^- \rightarrow 2O^{2-} \quad = \quad \text{reduction}$$

- These two equations are called electron-transfer, half-reaction equations.
- The balanced ionic equation for the reaction is

oxidation (loss of electrons)

$$2Mg \quad + \quad O_2 \longrightarrow 2Mg^{2+} \quad + \quad 2O^{2-}$$

reduction (gain of electrons)

Test yourself

1. State three different ways of defining reduction.
2. In each of the following, say which material is reduced and which is the reducing agent.
   (a) $CuO\ (s) + C\ (s) \rightarrow Cu\ (s) + CO\ (g)$
   (b) $H_2S\ (g) + Br_2\ (l) \rightarrow 2HBr\ (g) + S\ (s)$
   (c) $2Li\ (s) + Cl_2\ (g) \rightarrow 2LiCl\ (s)$
3. $Fe_2O_3\ (s) + 2Al\ (s) \rightarrow 2Fe\ (s) + Al_2O_3\ (s)$
   In this reaction, which material is
   (a) oxidised   (b) reduced
   (c) the oxidising agent   (d) the reducing agent?

[H]

4. What is a redox reaction?
5. In the following reaction, what is oxidised and what reduced?

   $$Cl_2 + 2Br^- \rightarrow 2Cl^- + Br_2$$

   Rewrite the reaction as two electron-transfer, half-reaction equations.
6. Calcium will burn in air to form calcium oxide. Explain, with equations, why this is a redox reaction.

Know the facts

- **Neutralisation** is the reaction between **acids** and **alkalis**.
- All acids have pH less than 7.

```
0                                    7
  Strong                     Weak
  acids  ⟵                   acids ↑
                                  Neutral
```

- **Bases** are oxides and hydroxides of metals.
- Acid + base → salt + water
- For example:

$$H_2SO_4 \ (aq) + CuO \ (s) \rightarrow CuSO_4 \ (aq) + H_2O \ (l)$$

- The vast majority of bases are insoluble in water.
- The few that are soluble are called alkalis.
- The two most common alkalis are:
  - sodium hydroxide, NaOH
  - potassium hydroxide, KOH
- Alkalis have pH greater than 7.

```
7  Weak                    Strong 14
↑  alkalis        ⟶        alkalis
Neutral
```

- Alkalis are bases and therefore react with acids.
- Acid + alkali → salt + water.
- For example:

$$HCl \ (aq) + NaOH \ (aq) \rightarrow NaCl \ (aq) + H_2O \ (l)$$

- The pH of the acid and alkali cancel each other out.
- The pH of the salt solution formed is 7 (neutral).
- For this reason the reaction between an acid and an alkali is called a neutralisation reaction.

[H]

Neutralisation reactions

- Dilute acids are excellent conductors of electricity. They must, therefore, consist mainly of ions.
- For example: dissolving hydrogen chloride gas in water to form hydrochloric acid causes ions to be produced.

$$HCl \ (g) \xrightarrow{\text{in water}} H^+ \ (aq) + Cl^- \ (aq)$$
hydrochloric acid

- The hydrogen ion (H^+) is present in all acids. It is responsible for the characteristic properties of acids.

- Similarly when soluble bases are dissolved in water, hydroxide ions (OH^-) are produced.

$$NaOH \ (s) \xrightarrow{\text{in water}} Na^+ \ (aq) + OH^- \ (aq)$$
sodium hydroxide solution

- When an acid reacts with an **alkali**, the H^+ ions of the acid combine with the OH^- ions of the alkali to form water molecules.
- This is the essence of a neutralisation reaction.
- The simplest ionic equation for neutralisation is:

$$H^+ \ (aq) + OH^- \ (aq) \rightarrow H_2O \ (l)$$

Test yourself

1 Give a definition of
  (a) an acid
  (b) an alkali.

2 What is 'neutralisation'? Why is it given this name?

[H]

3 For the reaction between sulphuric acid and potassium hydroxide, write
  (a) a balanced chemical equation
  (b) the simplest ionic equation.

4 For the reaction between potassium hydroxide and hydrochloric acid, write
  (a) a balanced chemical equation
  (b) the simplest ionic equation.

5 Dilute sulphuric acid is a very good conductor of electricity whereas very concentrated sulphuric acid is a poor conductor of electricity. What does this tell you about the ionisation of sulphuric acid?

63 Thermal decomposition

Know the facts

- **Decomposition** is the breaking down of a compound into two or more simpler substances.
- When this is brought about by heating, the process is called thermal decomposition.
- For example: if green copper carbonate powder is heated it decomposes easily into black copper oxide powder and carbon dioxide gas.

$$CuCO_3 \text{ (s)} \xrightarrow{\text{heat}} CuO \text{ (s)} + CO_2 \text{ (g)}$$

- Similarly, marble chips (calcium carbonate) decompose on heating.

$$CaCO_3 \text{ (s)} \xrightarrow{\text{heat}} CaO \text{ (s)} + CO_2 \text{ (g)}$$

Remember:
Reactive metals have stable compounds; less reactive metals have less stable compounds.

- The decomposition of calcium carbonate, however, is much more difficult than that of copper carbonate. It requires much more heat. This is because calcium is a much more reactive metal than copper and therefore its compounds are much more stable.
- Note that the stable compounds of the very reactive metals which cannot be decomposed by heat can often be decomposed by electricity when they are molten.
- For example:

$$NaCl \xrightarrow{\text{heat}} \text{stable; no reaction}$$

whereas:

$$2NaCl \text{ (l)} \xrightarrow{\text{electricity}} 2Na \text{ (s)} + Cl_2 \text{ (g)}$$

Test yourself

1 What is meant by 'decomposition'?

2 What is meant by 'thermal decomposition'?

3 Write a balanced equation for the thermal decomposition of magnesium carbonate and name all the products.

4 Explain why sodium carbonate will not decompose when heated.

5 Potassium chloride will not decompose when heated.
   (a) What does this tell you about potassium?
   (b) How could potassium chloride be decomposed? Write an equation for the reaction.

64 Enzymes

Know the facts

- **Enzymes** are **proteins** contained in the human body.
- They catalyse the body's chemical reactions.
- Each enzyme is specific and catalyses one reaction.
- A living cell may contain a thousand enzymes.
  Remember:
  Catalysts alter the rate of a reaction; they are not chemically changed.
- Examples:
  – Amylase is found in saliva. It catalyses the conversion of starch to sugars.
  – Pysozyme catalyses the breakdown of sugars in bacteria. This breakdown destroys the bacteria.
- Enzymes work by fitting into the reactant molecule like a jigsaw piece. They will not fit into any other molecule.

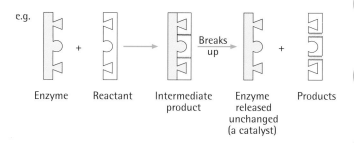

e.g.

Enzyme + Reactant → Intermediate product — Breaks up → Enzyme released unchanged (a catalyst) + Products

- Enzymes are pH- and temperature-sensitive. They work best at 40°C and pH 6.5. There is a rapid decline in effectiveness outside 35–45°C and pH 6.0–7.0.
- Enzymes are widely used in industry, for example, in fermentation, cheese making, pharmaceuticals manufacture and vitamin production.
- Their most familiar use is in biological washing powders. In these, enzymes called proteases break down proteins in the substances that stain clothes such as oil, dirt, gravy and blood.

Test yourself

1 What are enzymes and where are they found?

2 What function do enzymes fulfil?

3 How do enzymes work?

4 Name two enzymes.

5 Why are some washing powders described as 'biological'? How do they work?

65 Patterns and predictions

Know the facts

- Scientists use the study of materials and their reactions to find rules and patterns that enable predictions to be made.

Types of reaction (see topics 60–63)
- Knowing about **combustion**, **redox reactions**, **decomposition** and reactions of **acids** and **alkalis** enables you to predict behaviours.

Q What happens when sodium is burned in air?

A Burning (combustion) means combining with oxygen, therefore sodium oxide will be formed

$$4Na\ (s) + O_2\ (g) \rightarrow 2Na_2O\ (s)$$

Q What happens when dilute sulphuric acid reacts with magnesium?

A When an acid reacts with a metal

acid + metal → salt + hydrogen,

therefore

$$H_2SO_4\ (aq) + Mg\ (s) \rightarrow MgSO_4\ (aq) + H_2\ (g)$$

Q What happens when zinc carbonate is heated?

A When the compounds of the less reactive metals are heated alone they decompose, therefore

$$ZnCO_3\ (s) \xrightarrow{heat} ZnO\ (s) + CO_2\ (g)$$

The reactivity series of metals (see topic 39 on page 31)
- Knowing the position of a metal in the **reactivity series** of metals allows you to predict:
  - how it will react with air, water and acids
  - if it will displace another metal from solution
  - how easy or difficult it will be to extract from its ores and how this will best be done.

The periodic table (see topic 52 on page 41)
- Knowing the position of an element in the **periodic table** gives information about its physical and chemical properties.

Q Element X has atomic number 12. What predictions can you make about the element from this?

A Atomic number 12 means 12 protons and therefore 12 electrons in atoms of X. This gives an electronic configuration of 2.8.2.

The element therefore:
- is in group II of the periodic table
- will have the physical properties of metals, that is, high melting point, conductor of heat and electricity, etc.
- will have the chemical properties of metals, that is, will burn in air, react with acids, form ionic compounds, etc.

[H]
- is a metal which reacts by losing two electrons to form X^{2+} ions.

Test yourself

1 Predict the word equation and write a balanced chemical equation for each of the following:
   (a) the combustion of zinc powder
   (b) the reaction of copper oxide with hydrogen.

2 Element Y has an atomic number of 8.
   (a) What is its electronic configuration?
   (b) To which group of the periodic table does it belong?
   (c) Is it a metal or a non-metal?

[H]
   (d) Will it form ions? If so, write the symbol of the ions formed.
   (e) Will it react with hydrogen? If it does, will the compound formed be ionic or covalent? Explain your answer.

3 Zinc is above copper but below magnesium in the reactivity series.

   For each of the following pairs write the word equation if you predict they react and 'no reaction' if you predict they will not.
   (a) magnesium and zinc sulphate solution
   (b) copper and zinc sulphate solution
   (c) zinc and copper sulphate solution
   (d) copper and magnesium sulphate solution

Know the facts

- Reactions proceed at different rates.
- An explosion is a very fast reaction. Rusting is a very slow reaction.
- The collision theory states that:

  For reactant particles to react together they must

  1 collide with each other

  2 collide with sufficient energy to react rather than just bounce away. This is activation energy.

- Conditions which change the number of occurrences of 1 and 2, change the rate of the reaction.
- That is, the rate of a reaction is dependent on the number of fruitful collisions per unit time.

Temperature and rate

- Heating particles gives them energy hence they move faster and collide more often.
- Because the collisions are at higher energy levels, more are fruitful.
- Hence rate increases as temperature increases.

Concentration and rate

- If one or more of the reactants is in solution, then increasing the **concentration** increases the number of particles available.
- This will increase the number of fruitful collisions and hence rate.
- For example:

  $Mg\ (s) + 2HCl\ (aq) \rightarrow MgCl_2\ (aq) + H_2\ (g)$

  If the hydrochloric acid solution is dilute the reaction will be much slower than if it were concentrated.
- Hence rate increases as concentration increases.

Surface area and rate

- Reactions involving solids are much faster if the solid is used in small pieces or is powdered.
- For example:

  $CaCO_3\ (s) + 2HCl\ (aq) \rightarrow CaCl_2\ (aq) + H_2O\ (l) + CO2\ (g)$

  This reaction is much faster if smaller pieces of marble chip are used. Powdered marble chip reacts very quickly.
- The reason for this is that when the solid is powdered far more atoms are exposed to the acid and hence the number of fruitful collisions increases.
- Rate increases with increasing surface area.

Catalyst

- Some reactions can be speeded up by adding a catalyst.
- The **catalyst** does not increase the number of collisions but works by reducing the activation energy needed for fruitful collisions.
  The graph below shows this:

Remember:
A catalyst alters the rate of a reaction without itself being changed in any way.

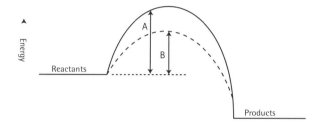

Test yourself

1 Apart from explosions and rusting, give an example of:

   (a) a fast reaction

   (b) a slow reaction.

2 According to the collision theory, what are the requirements for particles to react?

3 (a) What is the effect of increasing concentration on rate of reaction?

   (b) What is the effect of lowering temperature on rate of reaction?

   (c) What is the effect of using large pieces of marble chip in reaction with hydrochloric acid?

   (d) How do catalysts speed up reactions?

4 Catalysts can be used to slow down reactions. They are then called inhibitors. How do you think they might work?

Know the facts

- Most chemical reactions become either hotter or colder as they proceed.
- These temperature changes are associated with energy changes when bonds are broken or made.

  Remember:
  Breaking bonds, energy in.
  Making bonds, energy out.

- Reactions begin by breaking the bonds between atoms in the reactants. To do this, energy must be put in.
- When products are formed new bonds are made and then energy is released.
- If less energy has to be put in to break reactant bonds than is given out when making product bonds, then, overall, energy is released from the reaction. This is an exothermic reaction.
- If more energy is needed to break bonds than is released in making bonds, then, overall, energy is taken in by the reaction. This is an endothermic reaction.
- The energy changes associated with chemical reactions can be represented on energy level diagrams.

Exothermic reactions
- Here the energy content of the reactants is greater than the energy content of the products.
- More energy is given out in bond formation than is used in bond breaking.

Endothermic reactions
- Here the situation is exactly the reverse of the above.

The heat of reaction
- The heat change is called the **heat of reaction** and has the symbol ΔH which means **change in heat**.
- ΔH is measured in kilojoules per mole (kJ/mole).
- In exothermic reactions the change in heat is downwards and ΔH is negative.
- In endothermic reactions ΔH is positive.

Test yourself

1 The equation for the burning of natural gas (methane, CH_4) is

$$CH_4\ (g) + 2O_2\ (g) \rightarrow CO_2\ (g) + 2H_2O\ (g)$$

Heat is given out and therefore the reaction is exothermic.

(a) Which has the greater heat content, methane and oxygen, or carbon dioxide and steam?

(b) Draw a labelled energy level diagram for this reaction.

(c) Is ΔH positive or negative? Explain your answer.

2 When nitrogen and hydrogen make ammonia the equation is

$$N_2\ (g) + 3H_2\ (g) \rightarrow 2NH_3\ (g)$$

(a) Which and how many bonds have to be broken?

(b) Which and how many bonds are formed?

(c) ΔH is negative for this reaction. Explain fully what this tells you about the energy changes associated with the reaction.

3 Given that:

$$H_2\ (g) \rightarrow 2H\ (g) \qquad \Delta H = +436\ kJ/mole$$
$$Br_2\ (g) \rightarrow 2Br\ (g) \qquad \Delta H = +224\ kJ/mole$$
$$H\ (g) + Br\ (g) \rightarrow HBr\ (g) \quad \Delta H = -366\ kJ/mole$$

(a) calculate ΔH for the reaction

$$H_2\ (g) + Br_2\ (g) \rightarrow 2HBr\ (g)$$

(b) Is this reaction exothermic or endothermic?

Know the facts

- Ammonia is manufactured in the Haber process.

  $$N_2 (g) + 3H_2 (g) \rightarrow 2NH_3 (g)$$

- The process is affected by ammonia being easily decomposed.

  $$2NH_3 (g) \rightarrow N_2 (g) + 3H_2 (g)$$

- This means the reaction can go in either direction. It is reversible.

- The reaction is exothermic and the complete equation is

  $$N_2 (g) + 3H_2 (g) \rightleftharpoons 2NH_3 (g) \quad \Delta H \text{ is negative}$$

- In a **reversible reaction** both forward and backward reactions take place simultaneously.

- When the rate of the forward reaction equals the rate of the backward reaction there is no change in the amounts of the reactants and products. At this point, the reaction has reached **equilibrium**.

- The position of equilibrium tells you amounts of the reactants and products present at equilibrium. For example, there may be, say, 20% NH_3 and 80% N_2/H_2 at equilibrium, or here may be 40% NH_3, 60% N_2/H_2, etc.

- The position of equilibrium can be changed by changing the conditions of the reaction.

- Predicting the effect on position of equilibrium of changing the conditions is governed by Le Chatelier's principle. This states that the equilibrium will move to oppose or nullify any change made.

The best (optimum) conditions for the Haber process
1 Temperature

- If the temperature is increased, Le Chatelier's principle says the system will try to absorb the heat. The backward reaction is favoured and there is a decrease in ammonia yield.

- However, increasing temperature will increase the number of collisions and hence rate.

- High temperature therefore means high rate but low yield.

2 Pressure

- If pressure is increased, Le Chatelier's principle says the system will absorb the increase by going to smaller volume. The forward reaction is favoured because there are fewer molecules on the right of the equation.

- Increase in pressure also pushes molecules closer together, which increases collisions and therefore rate.

  High pressure means high rate and high yield.

3 Catalyst

- Using a **catalyst** will not affect the position of equilibrium but will increase rate.

Summary

The conditions usually chosen to give the best compromise between yield, rate and cost are:

$$N_2 (g) + 3H_2 (g) \xrightleftharpoons[\substack{500-550°C \\ \text{Fe catalyst}}]{\text{250 atmospheres}} 2NH_3 (g), \quad \Delta H \text{ is negative}$$

This yields about 15% conversion at equilibrium.

The contact process

- Another example of a reversible industrial process is the contact process for the manufacture of sulphuric acid.

- Part of this process involves the reaction

  $$2SO_2 (g) + O_2 (g) \rightleftharpoons 2SO_3 (g), \quad \Delta H \text{ is negative}$$

- See also topic 45 on page 35.

Test yourself

1. What is a reversible reaction?
2. What is meant by 'equilibrium'?
3. What is meant by 'position of equilibrium'?
4. In the reaction

   $$A + B \rightleftharpoons C + D \qquad \Delta H \text{ is negative}$$

   what is the effect of decreasing the temperature on the position of equilibrium? Explain your answer.

5. Nitrogen and hydrogen are left to reach equilibrium in a sealed container. What will be the effect on the position of equilibrium of:

   (a) increasing temperature

   (b) increasing container size

   (c) inserting a catalyst

   (d) removing ammonia

   (e) removing nitrogen?

   Explain your answers.

69 Electric current and voltage

Know the facts 🔑

- Electric current transfers energy round a circuit.
- An **electric current** is a flow of charge and is measured in **amps** (A).
- Electric current is measured with an ammeter, which is placed in the circuit in series.
- The current is the same all the way round a series circuit.
- In a parallel circuit the current flowing into a junction is the same as the current flowing out.

- A current only passes through a component or wire if there is a voltage across it.
- Voltage is measured by placing a voltmeter in parallel with a component.
- **Voltage** tells us the difference in the energy carried by the charge between two points.

Test yourself 🔑

1 Draw a circuit to measure the current through a lamp. Add a voltmeter to your circuit to measure the voltage across the lamp.

2 Write down the current passing points A and B in the circuit shown below.

[H]

3 A battery supplies 150 coulombs in 5 minutes.
   (a) What was the current in the circuit?
       The current supplied 900 joules in 5 minutes.
   (b) What was the voltage of the battery?

70 Resistance

Know the facts 🔑

- Changing the **resistance** in the circuit changes the current.
- Increasing the resistance decreases the current.
- Resistance is measured in ohms (Ω).

$$\text{resistance } (\Omega) = \frac{\text{voltage (volts)}}{\text{current (amps)}}$$

- It is also useful to think of this equation as

  voltage (volts) = current (amps) × resistance (Ω)

  or

  $V = IR$

- Connecting wires are designed to have low resistance.
- Some wires are designed to have resistance.
  - The longer the wire the greater the resistance.
  - The thinner the wire the greater the resistance.

Test yourself 🔑

1 Write down the equation that links voltage, current and resistance.

2 In the circuit a current of 2 A passes through the 5 Ω resistor. Calculate the voltage across the resistor.

3 A variable resistor is used to change the current through a lamp.
   (a) Draw a circuit to show how the lamp, variable resistor and battery should be connected.

[H]
   (b) Explain why the brightness of the lamp increases when the current increases.

4 A resistor has 12 V across it when 0.25 A passes through it. Calculate the value of the resistance.

71 Components in circuits

Know the facts 📖

- Components are included in circuits to control the current.
- A current–voltage graph shows how the current in a component changes as the voltage across it changes.

- A resistor at constant temperature has a constant resistance.

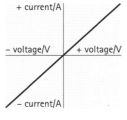

- The filament in a lamp becomes hotter as the voltage across it increases. As it becomes hotter its resistance increases.

- A **diode** only allows current to pass one way. When the voltage is reversed no current passes.
- The resistance of a **thermistor** changes with temperature. The resistance of the thermistor decreases as the temperature increases. Thermistors are used to detect temperature changes.
- The resistance of a light dependent resistor (**LDR**) decreases as the light level increases.
- See page 77 for the symbols used for the components in circuits.

Test yourself 📖

1 Describe how the resistance of a lamp changes as the current in the lamp increases.

2 Describe how the current through a diode changes as the voltage rises from −5 V to +5 V.

[H]

3 (a) What happens to the resistance of an LDR in a circuit as the light gets brighter?

  (b) What effect will this have on the current in the circuit?

72 Electrical power and energy

Know the facts 📖

- Batteries, solar cells and generators are all sources of energy. Electric current transfers the energy from the source to the circuit.
- Resistors become warm when a current passes through them.
- The rate at which energy is transferred to the circuit is the **power**.
- **Power** is measured in watts (W) and kilowatts (kW).
- 1 kW = 1000 W.
- You calculate electrical power using the equation:
    power (watts) = voltage (volts) × current (amps).
- You calculate the energy transferred using the equation:
    energy transferred (joules) = power (watts) × time (seconds).

Test yourself 📖

1 An immersion heater is connected to a 12 V supply. The current in the circuit is 3 A. The heater operates for 5 minutes.

  (a) Calculate the power transferred from the supply to the circuit.

  (b) Calculate the energy transferred from the supply to the heater in 5 minutes.

[H]

  (c) Calculate the resistance of the heater.

2 A vacuum cleaner connected to the mains supply is rated at 2 kW and operates from the 230 V mains supply.

  (a) What is 2 kW in watts?

  (b) How much energy would be transferred from the mains supply to the vacuum cleaner in 10 minutes?

[H]

  (c) What would be the current in the vacuum cleaner circuit?

69

70

71

72

Know the facts

- The current from batteries is a **direct current** (d.c.). It always flows in the same direction and does not change in size.

- Mains electricity supplies an **alternating current** (a.c.). The current is constantly changing size and direction. The direction changes fifty times per second; the frequency is 50 Hz.

| Current from a battery | Alternating current |

- Electric current is supplied to the home through the live wire and returns through the neutral wire. In normal use the earth wire does not carry a current.

- The wires in the mains cable are insulated to make sure that no current passes between the live, neutral and earth wires.

- Fuses and circuit breakers are designed to break the circuit if the current is too big. This prevents damage to appliances and stops wiring overheating.

- If there is a fault in an appliance and the metal part becomes live a large current might pass through you to reach earth. For this reason the metal parts of most appliances are connected to the earth wire. Now the large current will blow the fuse or trip the circuit breaker. A circuit breaker will cut the circuit more quickly than a fuse.

- Some appliances have plastic casing with no metal showing. The plastic insulation provides protection from a shock. The appliance is double insulated. The appliance does not need an earth wire.

- The energy you use has to be paid for. An electricity meter measures the energy used in kilowatt-hours (kWh).

- You can calculate the energy used by an appliance using the equation:

    energy (kilowatt-hours) = power (kW) × time (hours).

- The electricity bill tells you the cost of a unit of electricity, currently about 8 pence per unit.

Test yourself

1 A lamp is rated at 250 W. What is this power rating in kW?

2 (a) How much energy, in kWh, is used by a 2 kW fire if it is switched on for 3 hours?

  (b) What is the cost of using the fire if the price of electricity is 8 pence per unit?

3 Explain how a fuse helps to prevent fire caused by electrical faults.

4 Explain why a double insulated device does not need an earth wire.

5 An electric iron is rated at 2.3 kW. and connected to a 230 V supply.

  (a) What current will flow in the circuit when the iron is warming up?

  (b) What fuse rating should be used with the iron: 1 A, 5 A or 13 A? Give a reason for your answer.

Know the facts

- Some materials when rubbed together become charged. **Electrons** have been transferred from one material to the other.
- If the materials are **insulators** the charge does not leak away. This is sometimes called static charge.
- The object that loses electrons will be positively charged. The object that gains electrons will be negatively charged.
- Two objects with the same charge repel each other.
- Two objects with different charges attract each other.

- An electric current is a flow of charge.
- In a wire an electric current is a flow of electrons.
- Some chemical compounds conduct electricity when the compound is molten or dissolved in water.
- The electric current in an **electrolyte** is carried by positive and negative **ions** (see topic 37 on page 29).

[H]
- Electric charge (coulombs) = current (amps) × time (seconds).

Test yourself

1 When Jon rubs the balloons on his jumper the balloons gain electrons.

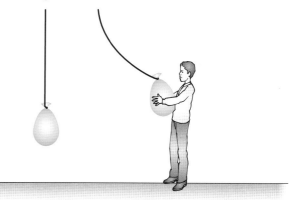

(a) What is the charge on the balloons called?

(b) Is the charge on Jon's jumper positive or negative?

(c) Draw a diagram to show what happens when the two balloons hang from the strings. Explain your answer.

2 Explain why your hair might stand on end when you have pulled a jumper over your head. Use your ideas about electric charge in your answer.

[H]
3 A battery is connected to a 36 W lamp for 5 minutes. The current in the circuit is 3 A.

(a) Calculate how much charge passes through the lamp in 5 minutes.

(b) Calculate how much energy is transferred from the battery to the lamp in 5 minutes.

(c) Calculate how much energy each coulomb of charge carries to the lamp.

(d) What is the voltage of the battery?

73

74

Know the facts 📖

- Electric charge is used to remove ash from the smoke in a coal-fired power station.

  The ash particles have positive and negative ions attached. The particles are attracted to electrodes in the chimney.

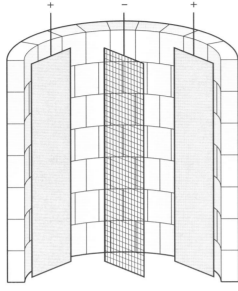

- Petrol passing along an aircraft refuelling pipe causes enough friction to give the pipe a static charge.

  If the charge builds up there is a danger of sparking and the risk of an explosion.

  The pipe is connected to earth so that the charge can leak away safely.

Test yourself 📖

1 Explain why you sometimes get an electric shock when you touch a door handle after walking across a carpet.

2 Explain why dust collects on a television screen much more than anywhere else in a room.

[H]

3 Explain why a charged balloon can be made to stick to a wall.

Know the facts 📖

- When a current-carrying wire is at right angles to a **magnetic field** there is a force on the wire.

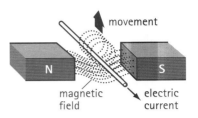

- There is a magnetic field round a wire that carries an electric current. This field interacts with the field due to the magnets. The wire is forced upwards.

- The field, the wire and the force are all at right angles.

- A simple electric motor has a coil of wire in a magnetic field. When a current flows the motor spins.

Test yourself 📖

1 Complete the following sentences.

  To make the force on the wires bigger and the motor spin faster you can make the current _____; or have _____ turns on the coil or use _____ magnets.

  To make the force move the wire in the opposite direction you can reverse the _____ or reverse the _____.

[H]

2 Use your ideas about the forces on wires in magnetic fields to explain why the coil in a simple motor spins when a current passes through it.

Know the facts

- Moving a magnet into a coil produces a voltage across the ends of the coil.

When the magnet is pulled out the voltage is reversed.

When the magnet is stationary there is no voltage.

This effect is called **electromagnetic induction**.

- Electromagnetic induction also takes place in a transformer.

A changing current in the primary coil makes a changing magnetic field in the iron core.

A changing magnetic field in the iron core induces a changing voltage across the terminals of the secondary coil.

The greater the number of turns on the secondary coil the greater the voltage induced.

[H]

$$\frac{\text{voltage across primary}}{\text{voltage across secondary}} = \frac{\text{number of turns in primary coil}}{\text{number of turns in secondary coil}}$$

Test yourself

1 The north pole of a magnet is pushed into a coil and the needle on a voltmeter across the ends of the coil 'flicks' to the right.

What does the needle do when:

(a) the magnet remains still inside the coil

(b) the north pole of the magnet is pulled out of the coil

(c) the south pole of the magnet is pushed into the coil

(d) the south pole of the magnet is pulled out of the coil

(e) the south pole of the magnet is pushed into the other end of the coil?

2 Explain why a transformer only works when there is an **alternating current** (a.c.) in the primary coil.

[H]

3 A transformer is connected to a 300 V supply. There are 1200 turns on the primary coil and 40 turns on the secondary coil. What will be the output from the secondary coil?

Know the facts

Magnet rotates

Coil

Iron core

- A magnet spinning near a coil induces a voltage in the coil. This voltage is enough to light a lamp. A cycle dynamo works just like this.
- The faster you spin the magnet the greater the voltage induced.
- The more turns on the coil the greater the voltage induced.
- Scale up your spinning magnet, replace the spinning magnet with an electromagnet and you have the generator for a power station.
- Electricity is generated in power stations.
- In most power stations **fossil fuels** are burned to heat water to make steam which turns turbines.
- The turbines spin the generators that produce electricity.
- The electricity is carried around the country through a network of cables, the National Grid.
- Although the cables are good **conductors**, they are very long and have some **resistance**.
- As the electricity passes through the cables they warm up and some energy is lost. The greater the current, the greater the energy loss in the wires.
- To reduce energy losses **transformers** are used to step up the electricity to a high voltage and low current.
- Before the electricity is supplied to a town it is stepped down to 230 V.

Test yourself

1 Why is the spinning magnet in a cycle dynamo like a magnet being pushed in and out of a coil?

2 Explain why using transformers to step up the transmission voltage means the mains electricity supply is a.c.

3 We depend on fossil fuels for our electricity supply. Suggest three reasons why we should look for alternative energy sources.

4 Look at the diagram at the top of the page. Describe three places where energy is lost between burning the coal and the energy delivered to the house.

[H]

5 A power station generates 200 MW of electrical power at 25 000 V.

(a) Calculate the current in the cables.

A transformer steps the voltage up to 400 000 V.

(b) Calculate the new current in the cables if there is no energy lost in the transformer.

79 Distance and speed

Know the facts 📜

- If an object moves in a straight line the average **speed** of the object can be calculated using the equation

  average speed (m/s) = $\dfrac{\text{distance travelled (m)}}{\text{time taken (s)}}$

distance

speed x time

- You measure speed in metres per second (m/s).
- A distance–time graph for a cycle ride tells you about the journey. The steeper the graph, the shorter the time the cyclist took to cover the distance, so the faster the cyclist was moving.

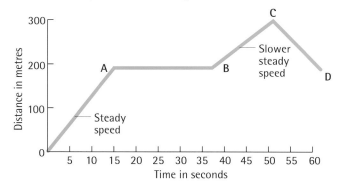

- The **velocity** of an object tells us the direction as well as the speed of the moving object. For example: an air-traffic controller needs to know the direction in which an aircraft is moving as well as its speed.

Test yourself 📜

1 A car travels 500 metres in 20 seconds. What is its average speed?

2 Look at the distance–time graph for a cyclist above.

  (a) Calculate the average speed between O and A.

  (b) What do you think happened between A and B?

  (c) Calculate the average speed between B and C.

  (d) What happened to the cyclist between C and D?

80 Acceleration

Know the facts 📜

- **Acceleration** tells you how much the **velocity** of an object changes each second.
- You can calculate acceleration using the equation:

  acceleration (m/s²) = $\dfrac{\text{change in velocity (m/s)}}{\text{time taken (s)}}$

- You measure acceleration in metres per second every second (m/s²).
- A velocity–time graph can give you information about a bus journey. The steeper the line, the greater the change in velocity during that time, so the greater the acceleration.

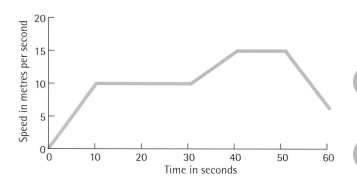

Test yourself 📜

1 In some data about cars one car is listed as going from 0 m/s to 30 m/s in 6 seconds. What is the average acceleration?

2 Look at the velocity–time graph for the bus. Describe the journey, saying whether the bus is accelerating, decelerating or moving at a steady speed. Give as much information as you can about the journey.

3 A rocket accelerates away from its launch pad and after 5 seconds it is moving at 40 m/s. What is its average acceleration?

[H]

4 A car moves off with an average acceleration of 2.5 m/s² for 8 seconds. How fast will it be moving after this time?

Know the facts

- Gravitational forces are felt near any massive object, such as the Sun, Moon or other planets.

- The force of **gravity** on an object is its weight.

- The **weight** of an object depends on its **mass** and the strength of the gravitational field.

- Weight is a force and is measured in newtons (N).

  weight = mass × gravitational field strength
  (N)   (kg)   (N/kg)
  $W = mg$

- Frictional forces resist the movement of the object over a surface or through a liquid or gas.

- When two objects are in contact they exert equal and opposite forces on each other.

- Forces come in pairs. When you sit on a chair, you push down on the cushion, compressing the springs in the cushion; the cushion pushes up on you. If it did not, you would fall through the chair onto the floor!

- When the forces on an object are balanced the object will remain as it is: stationary or moving at a steady speed in a straight line.

- When the forces on an object are unbalanced the object might :
  - start to move in the direction of the force
  - speed up (accelerate) or slow down (decelerate)
  - change direction.

- When an unbalanced force acts on an object to make it accelerate:

  the greater the force, the greater the acceleration
  the greater the mass, the smaller the acceleration.

- To calculate the effect of a force on an object you can use this equation:

  force (N) = mass (kg) × acceleration (m/s²)
  $F = ma$

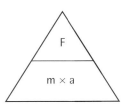

- You can use arrows to show the direction of the force and its size; the longer the arrow the greater the force.

Test yourself

1 Look at the pictures below. The arrows show the direction and relative size of the forces acting on each object. Write down whether you think each object is accelerating, decelerating or moving at a steady speed.

2 A car of mass 1500 kg accelerates from 0 m/s to 20 m/s in 10 seconds.

 (a) Calculate the acceleration of the car.

 (b) Calculate the force needed to give this acceleration.

3 A cyclist and her bike have a total mass of 80 kg. What force is needed to give an acceleration of 0.5 m/s²?

4 An aircraft with a mass of 12 000 kg needs an acceleration of 3 m/s² to reach take-off speed before the end of the runway. What is the unbalanced force needed to give this acceleration?

82 Stopping a car

Know the facts 📖

- The force needed to stop a car depends on the speed of the car and the mass of the car plus its occupants.
- The braking distance is the distance a car travels between the time when the brakes are applied and when the car comes to a halt.
- The thinking distance is the distance a car travels between the time when the driver realises the brakes must be applied and when the brakes actually go on. The thinking distance depends on the speed of the car and the reaction time of the driver.
- When a car has a head-on collision with a concrete bollard both will be damaged. The car exerts a force on the bollard. The bollard exerts an equal and opposite force on the car. This is another example of forces coming in pairs.

Test yourself 📖

A car is travelling at 30 m/s. The driver has a reaction time of 0.5 s.

1 Calculate the thinking distance at this speed.

2 What would be the effect on this thinking distance if the driver were tired? Explain your answer.

The braking distance required for this car to slow down from 30 m/s to 0 m/s is 64 m.

3 What is the total stopping distance?

4 What might be the effect on the stopping distance if the road were wet? Explain your answer.

If the car runs into a bollard the stopping time would be very short.

5 Would the stopping force be greater or smaller than the braking force? Explain your answer.

6 How would the stopping force be different if the bollard were replaced with a cushioned wall of tyres?

83 Falling objects

Know the facts 📖

- An object falls because **gravity** pulls it.
- The force of gravity gives the object an **acceleration.**
- This is called the acceleration due to gravity, g.
- On Earth $g = 9.8$ m/s^2. (You can usually use $g = 10$ m/s^2 in calculations.)
- When objects fall through air, there is also air **resistance** acting on them.
- The amount of air resistance depends on how fast the object is falling and its shape.
- As a falling object speeds up its air resistance increases too until, eventually, the pull of gravity (its weight) is balanced by the air resistance. It stops accelerating and falls at a steady speed, called its **terminal velocity**.
- The greater the weight of the object, the greater the air resistance needs to be to balance it.

Test yourself 📖

1 Complete the following sentences.

A falling object is pulled towards the Earth by _____. This force is called the _____ of the object. An object falling through air will experience air resistance. Air resistance depends on the _____ of the object and its _____ . When the air resistance is equal to the weight of the object the object will stop _____ and will move at a steady _____ , called its terminal velocity.

2 Look at the pictures of the falling parachutist.

(a) Describe how the speed of the parachutist will change as she falls.

(b) Suggest what difference it would make to the motion of the parachutist if she weighed a lot less.

Know the facts

- There are many kinds of waves: light waves, sound waves, waves on water and waves along a rope.
- All these waves carry energy; all have properties in common including **reflection**, **refraction** and **diffraction**.
- When a wave hits a barrier it is reflected back. You see exactly the same when light is reflected from a mirror.
- The **angle of incidence** is equal to the **angle of reflection**.

 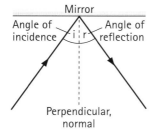

- When a water wave passes into shallower water it is slowed down. This makes the wave change direction. This is called **refraction**.

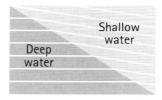

- You see exactly the same effect when light passes from air into water or glass. As the light slows down it is refracted towards the normal.

- When the light passes from glass to air it speeds up and is refracted away from the normal.

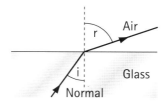

- As the angle of incidence inside the glass increases the amount of light refracted out decreases and more is reflected back inside the glass.
  At the **critical angle** the light is refracted through 90° and does not emerge.
  At angles greater than the critical angle the light is **totally internally reflected**.

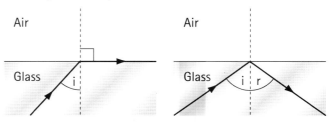

[H]

- When waves pass through a gap in a barrier they spread out on the other side. This is called **diffraction**.
- The spreading happens best when the size of the gap is about the same size as the wavelength of the wave.

Test yourself

1. Give an example of evidence that sound waves are reflected from hard surfaces.
2. Give an example of light changing direction as it passes from one medium to another.
3. Complete the ray diagram to show how total internal reflection is used to make these two prisms into a periscope.

Know the facts

Wavelength λ

Amplitude

- The **wavelength** λ of a wave is the distance from the crest of one wave to the crest of the next wave.

- The **frequency** *f* of a wave is the number of waves produced each second. The unit of frequency is hertz (Hz).

- The **amplitude** of a wave is the height of the wave from the crest to the mid-point where there is no displacement.

[H]
- wave speed (m/s) = frequency (Hz) × wavelength (m)

$$v = f\lambda$$

Transverse waves

- For example: when one end of a rope is moved up and down the rest of the rope begins to move up and down and energy is transmitted down the rope.

- The energy travels along the rope but the rope moves up and down.

Longitudinal waves

- For example: when one slinky coil is pushed back and forth it sends energy along the spring.

- This time the movement of the spring is in the same direction in which the energy travels.

Test yourself

1 Group the following waves into longitudinal and transverse waves.

> light waves   sound waves   water waves
> waves along a rope

2 Describe how to use a cork and a stone to show that waves on water transfer energy but not matter.

3 A loudspeaker makes a sound with a frequency of 165 Hz. The wavelength of the sound is 2 m. Calculate the speed of sound.

Know the facts

- When a ruler is set vibrating, the air ahead of the ruler is made to vibrate.

- The particles in the air transmit a sound wave through the air. This is a **longitudinal** wave.

- The energy carried by the wave causes your eardrum to vibrate and you hear the sound.

- Sound waves reflect well off hard surfaces. This is why you hear echoes.

- Bats use echoes to locate their food and to avoid flying into obstacles. Bats use sounds at frequencies above 20 000 Hz. These frequencies are too high for humans to hear.

- These very high frequencies are called ultrasound.

- Ultrasound is also used for 'looking' inside human bodies. The waves are reflected from internal organs and a computer is used to build up a picture of the inside of the body

Test yourself

1 Sound cannot travel through a vacuum. Explain why this is so.

2 A rubber band is set into vibration and makes 500 vibrations in 10 seconds. What is the frequency of the sound?

3 A bat sends out a signal. Its reflection returns from a moth 0.1 seconds later. The moth was 15 metres away. What is the speed of the sound?

[H]
4 Sound can be diffracted through gaps. Suggest some evidence that shows this. (Think about how you hear what is happening in other rooms in your house.)

84

85

86

Know the facts

- The **electromagnetic spectrum** is a family of waves that all travel at the same speed in a vacuum.
- These waves are called electromagnetic waves.

Test yourself

1 Suggest one reason why doctors prefer to use ultrasound rather than x-rays to image a baby in the womb.

2 Why should you take care not to stay in sunlight too long on a sunny day?

3 How can infrared cameras 'see' people and animals at night?

4 Why might people be concerned about the safety of mobile phones?

short wavelength 0.000 000 000 001 m **high frequency** 10^{20} Hz	**gamma rays**	• emitted by some radioactive materials (see topic 98) • used in medicine to kill cancer cells and to trace blood flow • used to kill harmful bacteria on food and surgical instruments • large doses may damage human cells
	x-rays	• pass through soft tissue but not bones or metals • used to kill cancer cells and to produce shadow images of bones • large doses may damage human cells
	ultraviolet	• causes tanning of the skin • large doses may cause skin cancer
medium wavelength 0.000 000 5 m	**violet** **visible light** **red**	• detected by the eye • used for vision and photography • used through optical fibres for viewing inside the human body and other inaccessible places
	infrared	• radiated from warm and hot objects and causes heating • used in grills, toasters and radiant heaters • used in remote control devices, security cameras and communication
	microwaves	• some wavelengths absorbed by water used in cooking, but can damage living cells • longer wavelengths used in radar, mobile phones and satellite communication
long wavelengths 1 m–100 000 m **low frequency** – 10^4 Hz	**radiowaves**	• broad range of wavelengths used in communication

Know the facts

- Modern communications use a broad spread of the **electromagnetic spectrum** to transmit information.
- Early **optical fibres** used total internal reflection to transmit light. Doctors use fibres like this to see inside patients.

- Modern fibres are so fine that infrared passes straight down the cable.
- Telephone companies use cables of optical fibres to transmit telephone calls, computer signals and television programmes.
- An optical fibre carries many more messages than a copper cable of similar thickness, and less energy is lost along the way.
- Microwaves are used to transmit telephone calls across the country from transmitter to transmitter.
- Microwaves travel in straight lines and the curvature of the Earth limits the distance between transmitters to about 40km.
- To get signals around the world microwaves carry the signals into space where an orbiting satellite picks up the signal and bounces it on its way. Television broadcasts are sent this way too. The dish on the outside of a house collects the signals from the satellite.
- Radiowaves have been used to send information for a hundred years. The long wavelengths are ideally suited for sending signals across the country. The waves **diffract** around buildings to reach most places.

- A recent revolution is the increasing use of digital signalling.
- A conventional telephone converts sound waves to a changing electrical signal whose pattern matches the original wave. This is called an **analogue signal**.

- Modern telephone systems convert the analogue electrical signal to a **digital signal**. The digital signal consists of a stream of numbers that describes how the analogue signal changes. E-mail and faxes are sent by digital signals too.
- Digital signals suffer less from interference.
- Using digital signals allows the optical fibre or radio wave to carry even more information, many television channels or lots of telephone conversations.

Test yourself

1 Give two advantages of using optical fibres rather than copper wire to transmit telephone information.
2 Give two advantages of using microwaves rather than cables to transmit long distance telephone calls.
3 Give two advantages of using digital signals to transmit information.

[H]
4 What property of radio waves enables them to pass around tall buildings?

87

88

89 Plate tectonics [H]

Know the facts

- The Earth has a layered structure.
- The thin outer part, called the lithosphere, is rigid and is about 70km thick.

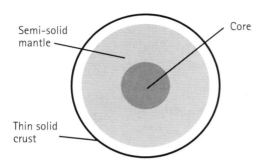

Semi-solid mantle

Core

Thin solid crust

- The lithosphere is broken into large plates that are moved by slow convection currents in the largely solid mantle beneath.
- Where the plates move apart, molten rock rises and solidifies to form new plate material.
- Where the plates move together mountains may form by folding, volcanoes may erupt and earthquakes occur.
- The rock record gives us evidence to support plate tectonic ideas.
  - Africa and South America have closely matching coastlines and the rocks and the fossil records suggest that they were once close together.
  - When new plate material forms under oceans, as the molten rock solidifies, it records the direction of the Earth's magnetic field. The magnetic patterns give us information about the way the plates have formed.

Test yourself

1 Two plates are moving apart under the Atlantic Ocean.
  - (a) What would you expect to see at the junction between the plates?
  - (b) What may happen as the convection currents move the plates apart?
2 What evidence is there that the plate tectonic theory is correct?

90 Waves through the Earth [H]

Know the facts

- Earthquakes occur when moving tectonic plates stick and then move suddenly. This happens at the earthquake **epicentre**.
- The shock from large earthquakes shakes the ground surface and can destroy buildings. Some of the energy is carried through the Earth by waves called **seismic waves.**
- Seismologists use information about the types of waves that are transmitted and how long they take to arrive at different 'listening stations' to learn more about the structure of the Earth.
- Seismic primary (P) waves are the fastest. They are **longitudinal waves** that can travel through solids, liquids and gases and can pass right through the Earth.

- Secondary (S) waves are slower **transverse waves**. Transverse waves can only pass through solids. They stop at the core, showing that the outer core is liquid.

- P waves are **refracted** at the junction between the mantle and the core. This means there are some parts of the Earth where P waves from a large earthquake do not arrive at all and other parts where they arrive late.

Test yourself

1 Give three differences between P waves and S waves.
2 Explain why there will be a significant time delay between the arrival of P waves and S waves at listening stations around the world. Where will the delay be longest?

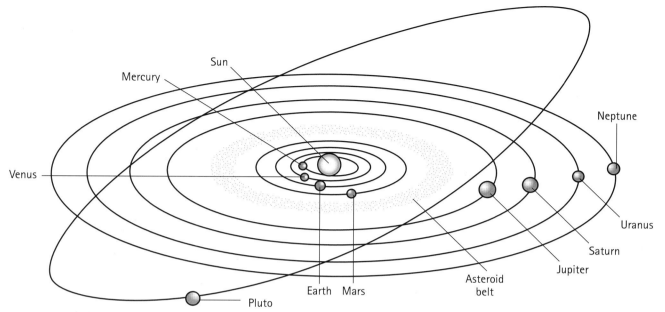

Sun
Mercury
Venus
Pluto
Earth Mars
Asteroid belt
Jupiter
Saturn
Uranus
Neptune

Know the facts

- The **Solar System** consists of the Sun, nine planets, the asteroid belt and a number of comets.
- All the planets except Pluto have orbits in the same plane.
- The orbit of each of the planets is an ellipse.
- The orbit of Pluto is a more elongated ellipse and is at an angle to the plane of the other planets.
- Between the four inner planets and the outer planets lies the asteroid belt, made up of dust and rocks.
- All the bodies orbiting the Sun are held in their orbit by **gravity**.
- The strength of the gravitational force depends on the mass of the body, the mass of the Sun and how close the body is to the Sun.
- The time a planet takes to orbit the Sun is its year.
- The further the planet is from the Sun, the weaker the pull of gravity. This means it moves more slowly and so its year is longer.
- The Moon is a natural **satellite** of the Earth. Other planets have satellites too.
- There are also many artificial satellites in orbit around the Earth. They too are held in orbit by gravity and the time taken to complete one orbit depends on their distance from the Earth.
- Comets make very eccentric orbits of the Sun, sometimes coming in close and fast and at other times travelling a long way, far beyond Pluto.

Test yourself

1 The diagram shows the three innermost planets of the Solar System.

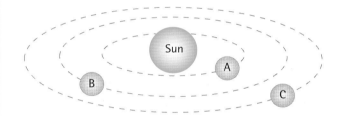

Sun
A
B
C

(a) Name the planet labelled B?
(b) Which planet has the shortest year, A, B or C?
(c) Draw on the diagram the path of a comet.
(d) Write an X on the comet's path where its speed is the greatest.

2 What is the name of the Earth's only natural satellite?

3 What force keeps this satellite in orbit around the Earth?

89
90
91

Know the facts

92

93

94

- The Sun is just one star in the **galaxy** called the Milky Way.
- You can see stars that are fairly close to the Earth as pinpoints of light. However, most of the Milky Way appears as a faint band of light in the night sky.
- Our galaxy is just one of many millions in the universe.
- Some galaxies appear as points of light in the night sky, others are so far away that they cannot be seen with the naked eye.
- Since the universe began, many stars have been formed and have died.
- Stars are formed when **gravity** pulls together massive clouds of dust and gas in space. As the mass falls together it gets hot. If it gets hot enough for hydrogen nuclei to fuse together to make helium, a star is formed.
- The **fusion** process releases energy keeping the core of the star hot.
- The force of **gravity** holds the star together against the enormous pressures caused by the high temperatures. The Sun is at this stable period in its life.

- As the hydrogen is used up in the fusion process, larger nuclei begin to be formed and the star may expand to become a red giant.
- When all the nuclear reactions are over, a small star, like our Sun, may begin to contract under gravity. It becomes a white dwarf as it fades and cools.
- With a larger, more massive star nuclear reactions may continue and the star will continue getting hotter and expanding until it explodes as a supernova.
- A supernova throws dust and gases into space, leaving a small dense neutron star, which shrinks to a black hole.
- Observations of other galaxies suggest that all the galaxies in the universe are moving apart very quickly. Those further away seem to be moving faster.
- The evidence suggests that the universe began with a big bang, which threw matter out in all directions.

Test yourself

1 How are stars formed?
2 What is the likely end to our star, the Sun?
3 Suggest what happens to the dust and gases thrown out by a supernova.

93 Energy and work

Know the facts

- When you lift a weight you do some **work**. If you lift a lot of weights your arms will remind you that you are doing a lot of work.
- You are transferring energy from your muscles to the weight.
- When you push a broken-down car along the road you are doing work.
- You have to exert a force to overcome the friction within the car engine and wheels and between the wheels and the ground.

- You measure work and energy in joules (J) and kilojoules (kJ).
- 1 kilojoule = 1000 joules.
- You can calculate the work done when a force moves something through a distance:

   work done (J) = force (N) × distance (m)

Test yourself

1 A builder uses a force of 250 N to carry a hod of bricks up 5 metres. How much work does she do?

2 A weightlifter raises 120 kg through 1.5 metres.

   (a) What force does she need to use to lift 120 kg?

   (b) How much work does she do in lifting the load 1.5 metres?

3 A car needs a force of 2000 N to pull a caravan.

   (a) How much work is done by the car in moving the caravan 200 m?

   (b) Give your answer in part (a) in kilojoules.

94 Power and efficiency

Know the facts

- A builder's mate who only carries one hod of bricks an hour up the ladder would not stay in the job very long. The rate of work is important too.
- Rate of work or energy transfer is called **power**.

> Q How much food does the labourer need to eat to do the job?
>
> A Well, it is certainly more than the work done.

- The labourer gets energy from the food she eats. Not all the energy from the food eaten is transferred to lifting loads.
- **Efficiency** tells you how much of the energy input becomes useful output.

$$\text{energy efficiency} = \frac{\text{useful energy output}}{\text{total energy input}}$$

Test yourself

1 A stair-lift can lift a 800 N man 2.0 m in 10 seconds.

   (a) How much work does the stair-lift do?

   (b) What is the power of the stair-lift?

   (c) Why would the stair-lift actually need more power from the electricity supply than this?

2 An athlete in training weighs 60 kg. She does 100 step-ups in 3 minutes. Each step lifts her body 20 cm.

   (a) What is her weight in newtons?

   (b) How far does she step up altogether in 3 minutes?

   (c) How much work does she do in 3 minutes?

   (d) What is the athlete's power?

Know the facts ✏

- When the builder carries the bricks up the ladder she is doing work.
- Energy is transferred from the food energy in her muscles to the bricks.
- The bricks store energy in the Earth's gravitational field. The bricks have gained **gravitational potential energy**.

> Q What happens to that potential energy if the builder drops the bricks?
>
> A The bricks fall to the ground, accelerating as they go. The moving bricks are said to have kinetic energy.
>
> Q What happens to the kinetic energy of the bricks when they hit the ground?
>
> A Some of the energy will break bonds within the bricks and the bricks will disintegrate; some of the energy is carried away by sound waves to the ears of the builder and some of the energy will shake the ground.

[H]

- You can calculate the gain in gravitational potential energy using the equation:

  potential = mass × gravitational × height
  energy (J)   (kg)   field   lifted
                      strength (N/kg)   (m)

  $$PE = mgh$$

- You can calculate the **kinetic energy** using the equation:

  kinetic energy (J) = $\frac{1}{2}$ × mass (kg) × speed^2 (m/s^2)

  $$KE = \frac{1}{2}mv^2$$

Test yourself ✏

1 For each of the pictures,
   (a) say whether the object has kinetic energy and/or gravitational potential energy.
   (b) explain where the energy came from to get the object to where it is now.

[H]

2 A student is filling shelves in a supermarket. Each can of beans weighs 500 g and has to be lifted 1.2 m on to the shelf. 200 cans need to be transferred from the box to the shelf.
   (a) What is the mass of one can in kg?
   (b) What is the weight of one can in newtons?
   (c) How much work does the student do in lifting one can on to the shelf?
   (d) How much work is done in lifting 200 cans on to the shelf?
   (e) The student does the job in 3 minutes. What was the average power during this time?

Know the facts

- When an object is warmer than its surroundings, energy is transferred from the object to the colder surroundings.
- This transfer often happens by conduction.
- Metals are good **conductors**. Most non-metals are not.
- Poor conductors are used as insulators. Insulators are sometimes used to keep something hot and sometimes to keep something cold.

Test yourself

1 Look at the pictures. For each object explain whether the part indicated by an arrow is a good insulator or a good conductor and explain why it is being used in that situation.

2 We spend a lot of money on energy to keep our houses warm.

(a) Describe three ways in which energy is lost from our homes in winter.

(b) How could we reduce these losses, and so reduce our energy bills?

Know the facts

- Most energy is supplied to our homes through the electricity supply, the National Grid.

Q Where does the energy come from to generate electricity?

A The biggest energy source for power stations is fossil fuels.

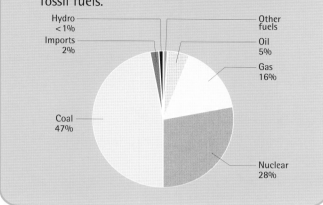

- **Fossil fuels** are burned in power stations to heat water to drive the turbines which turn the generators (see topic 78 on page 60).
- **Fossil fuels** are also used to transport both people and goods around the country.
- **Fossil fuels** are a finite resource. One day they will run out.

Test yourself

1 A car burns petrol to drive the engine. What has happened to the energy in the petrol by the end of a car journey?

2 A coal-fired power station has an efficiency of 35%. What does an efficiency of 35% mean?

3 There are other ways of driving generators than using steam turbines. Give two ways and suggest advantages and disadvantages of each.

4 It would be more energy-efficient for people to use public transport to travel to work.

(a) Explain why this is so.

(b) Give one other way in which city life would be better if more people used public transport.

(c) Suggest a reason why more people do not use public transport.

Radiation	What is it?	How far can it travel in air?	What stops it?	What happens in a magnetic field?
alpha α	particles – positive helium nuclei	a few centimetres	thin paper	small deflection
beta β	particles – negative electrons	a few metres	thin aluminium	large deflection
gamma γ	electromagnetic radiation	several kilometres	thick lead	no deflection

Know the facts

- **Radioactive decay** is a random process that takes place in the nuclei of some elements.
- The nuclei are unstable and spontaneously emit radiation that can ionise atoms and molecules.
- The radiation ionises the molecules in cells of the body. This may damage or even kill the cell.
- There are three kinds of radiation, alpha (α), beta (β) and gamma (γ).
- The **nucleus of an atom** is made of **protons** and **neutrons**.
- The protons are positively charged and the neutrons have no charge.
- Some nuclei are unstable because there are too many neutrons.
- When alpha or beta particles are emitted the proton number and neutron number change. This means a different element has been formed.
- Radioactivity is all around you. Some rocks are naturally radioactive; radioactive particles called cosmic rays come from the Sun and elsewhere in our galaxy.

- Both these sources of radiation give rise to radioactive particles in the air you breathe.

This radiation has always been there and is called **background radiation**.

You must remember to take background radiation into account when making radioactivity measurements.

Test yourself

1 What property of alpha and beta particles causes them to be deflected when they pass through a magnetic field?

2 Which radiation could reach us from outer space? Explain your answer.

3 How many protons and how many neutrons are there in an alpha particle?

4 Why would it be more dangerous to have an open source of gamma radiation in the room than a source of alpha or beta radiation?

5 Why would beta radiation be best for measuring the thickness of paper in a paper mill?

Know the facts

- **Radioactive decay** is a random process that makes the nucleus more stable.

- You cannot predict when a particular nucleus will decay. However, you can say that after a certain amount of time half the nuclei in a sample will have decayed.

- The time taken for half the nuclei to decay is called the half-life.

- As the nuclei decay there will be less of the material left to decay. Half of the remaining nuclei will decay in another **half-life**.

- The graph above shows how a sample of technetium decays.

- Technetium is used as a tracer in hospitals.

- The half-life of technetium is about 6 hours. Every six hours half the technetium decays, so the rate of decay decreases.

Test yourself

1 Look at the graph of technetium decay.

   (a) How long does it take the mass to change from 0.8g to 0.4g?

   (b) Does this agree with the statement that the half-life of technetium is 6 hours?

[H]

2 Uranium-235 is found in some igneous rocks. It decays to lead-207 with a half-life of 700 million years.
   Why is uranium-235 a good element to use for dating rocks?

Know the facts

- Care must be taken when handling radioactive materials. People who work with ionising radiation must take particular care; the greater the dose, the greater the risk of damage.

- However, there are ways of using ionising radiation to benefit people.

- Radiation damages cells. Careful application of radiation can be used to destroy cancerous cells, while leaving healthy cells unharmed. The radiation may be applied from a source outside the body or from within the body.

- Gamma radiation can be used in a similar way to x-rays to produce an image of the body. This is used in diagnosis.

- The ability of radiation to penetrate a known distance through materials is used to measure the thickness of a variety of materials in manufacturing.

Test yourself

1 In the picture, cobalt-60 is used as a source of gamma radiation to destroy cancerous cells. The source is directed at the tumour, but rotated in a circle and aimed at the body from different directions.

   (a) Explain why a gamma source is best for therapy from outside the body.

   (b) Suggest two reasons why the source is rotated around the body and not just aimed from one direction.

2 An isotope of iodine, iodine-131, is a beta-emitter. Explain why this is taken internally to treat cancer of the thyroid.

Some key formulae and reactions for chemistry

1. Some common names and formulae

Acids

hydrochloric acid HCl
sulphuric acid H_2SO_4
nitric acid HNO_3
carbonic acid H_2CO_3

> **Remember**
> Acid + Base - Salt + Water
> Acid + Metal - Salt + Hydrogen
> Acid + Carbonate - Salt + Water + Carbon Dioxide

Bases

copper oxide CuO
lead oxide PbO_2
magnesium oxide MgO
calcium oxide CaO

> **Remember**
> Bases are oxides and hydroxides of metals

alkalis {
calcium hydroxide $Ca(OH)_2$ - lime - water: goes milky with carbon dioxide
sodium hydroxide NaOH
potassium hydroxide KOH
ammonium hydroxide NH_4OH

> **Remember**
> An alkali is a soluble base

Salts

sodium chloride NaCl
copper sulphate $CuSO_4$
sodium carbonate Na_2CO_3
calcium carbonate $CaCO_3$ - limestone, marble chips
ammonium sulphate $(NH_4)_2SO_4$ } nitrogenous
ammonium nitrate NH_4NO_3 } fertilisers

Common Gases

oxygen O_2
ammonia NH_3
hydrogen chloride HCl
chlorine Cl_2
carbon dioxide CO_2

hydrogen sulphide H_2S
nitrogen N_2
carbon monoxide CO
hydrogen H_2
sulphur dioxide SO_2

Ores

haematite: iron (III) oxide, Fe_2O_3
copper pyrites: copper (I) sulphide, Cu_2S
bauxite: aluminium oxide Al_2O_3
zinc blende: zinc sulphide ZnS

2. Some organic compounds

methane	CH_4	vinyl chloride (chloroethene)	C_2H_3Cl
ethane	C_2H_6		
ethene	C_2H_4	chloroethane	C_2H_5Cl

ethanol	C_2H_5OH	aminoethane (ethylamine)	$C_2H_5NH_2$
ethanoic acid	CH_3COOH		

3. Some types of reaction

Combustion: burning in air or oxygen,
e.g. $2H_2 + O_2 \rightarrow 2H_2O$

Thermal decomposition: breaking down a compound by heat,
e.g. $CuCO_3 \xrightarrow{\text{heat}} CuO + CO_2$

Neutralisation: reacting an acid and an alkali together to give a salt solution which has pH7 (neutral),
e.g. $HCl + NaOH \rightarrow NaCl + H_2O$

Displacement: when a more reactive metal takes the place of a less reactive metal or a more reactive halogen takes the place of a less reactive halogen,
e.g. $Mg + ZnSO_4 \rightarrow MgSO_4 + Zn$
$Cl_2 + 2KBr \rightarrow 2KCl + Br_2$

Redox: when oxidation and reduction take place together in one reaction,
e.g.

$$CuO + H_2 \xrightarrow{\text{reduction / oxidation}} Cu + H_2O$$

Polymerisation: when small, single molecules (monomers) join into long chains (polymers),
e.g. $n\ C_2H_4 \rightarrow (C_2H_4)n$
ethene   polythene

Electrolysis: passing electricity through a molten ionic compound or an ionic compound in solution,
e.g.

$$2NaCl \xrightarrow[\text{molten}]{\text{electricity}} 2Na + Cl_2$$

Reversible reaction: a reaction which can proceed in either direction,
e.g. $N_2 + 3H_2 \rightleftharpoons 2NH_3$

Some key equations and symbols for physics

Electricity and magnetism

You should be able to use these relationships:

- voltage = current × resistance
  (volts)   (amps)   (ohms)
  $$V = IR$$

- electrical power = voltage × current
  (watts)   (volts)   (amps)
  $$P = VI$$

[H]

- charge = current × time
  (coulombs) (amps) (seconds)

- For a transformer:

$$\frac{\text{voltage across primary}}{\text{voltage across secondary}} = \frac{\text{number of turns in primary coil}}{\text{number of turns in secondary coils}}$$

You need to be able to use these relationships:

- power (watts) $= \dfrac{\text{work done or energy transferred (joules)}}{\text{time taken (seconds)}}$

- energy (kilowatt-hours) = power (kilowatts) × time (hours)

You should know these circuit symbols:

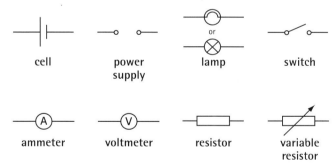

cell   power supply   lamp   switch

ammeter   voltmeter   resistor   variable resistor

Forces and motion

You should be able to use these relationships:

- average speed $= \dfrac{\text{distance travelled (m)}}{\text{time taken (s)}}$
  (m/s)

- average speed $= \dfrac{\text{change in velocity (m/s)}}{\text{time taken (s)}}$
  (m/s²)

- force = mass × acceleration
  (newtons) (kilograms)   (m/s²)
  $$F = ma$$

You need to be able to use the relationship:
[H]

- weight = mass × gravitational
  (newtons) (kilograms)   field strength
  $$W = mg \qquad \text{(N/kg)}$$

Waves

You should be able to use this relationship:
[H]

- wave speed = frequency × wavelength
  (m/s)   (hertz)   (metres)
  $$v = f\lambda$$

Energy

You should know and be able to use this relationship:

- energy = work = force × distance
  transferred   done   (newtons) (metres)
  (joules)

You need to be able to use these relationships:
[H]

- potential = mass × gravitational × height
  energy   (kg)   field strength lifted
  (J)   (N/kg)   (m)
  $$PE = mgh$$

[H]

- kinetic $= \frac{1}{2} \times$ mass × speed²
  energy   (kilograms) (m/s)²
  (joules)
  $$KE = \tfrac{1}{2} mv^2$$

- energy efficiency $= \dfrac{\text{useful energy output}}{\text{total energy input}}$

Biology

01 Cells

1 (a) Performs photosynthesis.
    (b) Controls all the activities in the cell.
    (c) Controls entry and exit of substances.

2 Chloroplasts, cell wall, cell vacuole.

3 Red blood cell.

02 Respiration

1 Lactic Acid.

2 Oxygen.

3 Alcoholic drinks or beer or wine or bread.

03 Enzymes

1 A biological catalyst.

2 (a) Liver.
    (b) Most froth is produced, therefore most enzyme, therefore more waste products, therefore cells are most active.

3 Temperature, pH.

4 No froth would be produced.

5 Average values will be more reliable, eliminating 'freak' results.

04 Diffusion and osmosis

1 (a) Osmosis involves passage of water only, never solutes or solutions; osmosis happens across a semi-permeable membrane.
    (b) Water is more concentrated in the soil solution than inside the cell vacuole because the cell sap contains more dissolved solutes than the soil solution. Water passes from where it is in high concentration (high water potential) to where it is in low concentration (low water potential) through a semi-permeable membrane (cell membrane).

2 If salt solution is added to the soil, there is a lower concentration of water inside the cell than outside, so there is a net flow of water out of the roots so the plant dies from dehydration.

3 Water passing into kidney tubules or water passing into guard cells of stomata in plants.

4 Air sacs of the lungs or at any tissue, e.g. muscles, from the blood in solution.

05 Cell division

1 (a) Mitosis.
    (b) Meiosis.

2 23.

3 Nucleus.

4 A = chromosome. B = cell membrane.

06 The digestive system

1 It increases the surface area for lipase to work.

2 It must be digested and made soluble.

3 (a) Stomach.
    (b) Mouth.
    (c) Colon.

4 (a) Stomach.
    (b) Mouth or duodenum.

5 (a) 2.5.
    (b) B
    (c) A requires acid. B requires alkali. If they were together they would neutralise each other.

07 Absorption of food

1 Small intestine (ileum).

2 The epithelium is very thin to allow for the passage of materials from the small intestine; the blood capillary allows for absorption and transport of digested nutrients except fats; the lacteal is for the transport of fats.

08 Blood

1 Red blood cell.

2 (a) Plasma.
    (b) Red blood cell.
    (c) Plasma and red blood cell.

3 B has a nucleus and is not round or A does not have a nucleus and is round (or biconcave or disc-shaped).

4 Glucose or amino acids or hormones or water or minerals or vitamins

5 Carbon dioxide passing into blood or oxygen passing into cells or water passing in both directions.

6 White cells ingest microbes. They also produce antibodies and antitoxins.

09 The heart

1 The left ventricle has to pump blood all around the body but the right ventricle only has to pump blood to the lungs.

2 To stop back-flow of blood into the atria.

3 (a) The pulse rate has increased during exercise so that more blood can be pumped to the muscles to supply them with glucose and oxygen. After the exercise the pulse rate gradually returns to normal.
    (b) The breathing rate would follow a similar pattern.
    (c) When the skin appears red, it means that its blood vessels have dilated (become wider) so that excess heat can be lost by radiation to keep the body temperature constant.

10 Breathing

1 In A, the diaphragm is flattened; in B the diaphragm is dome-shaped. In A the ribs have moved upwards; in B the ribs slope downwards.

2 (a) Decreases.
    (b) Increases.

11 Oxygen debt

1 Anaerobic.

2 (a) A: 95dm^3; B: 16dm^3.
    (b) The athletes need to repay the debt so they need to take in more oxygen than during norma activity.

3 Glucose $\rightarrow$ Lactic acid (+ Energy).

12 The eye

1 In bright light.

2 This would protect the retina from becoming damaged or allow vision in dim light.

3 Blinking protects the eye from damage by particles entering. Tear production: when your eyes 'water', special glands produce tears containing an antibacterial chemical to protect your eyes from infection.

4 Accommodation is the automatic process used by the eye to focus an image on the retina. To focus near objects, the ciliary muscles contract and the lens becomes more convex (thicker), making it of shorter focal length. To focus on distant objects, the ciliary muscles relax and the lens becomes less convex (thinner).

13 Reflex action

1 1 = receptor; 2 = sensory neurone; 3 = relay neurone; 4 = motor neurone; 5 = effector; 6 = grey matter.

2 Reflex actions are fast, automatic ways of protecting you from danger.

3 Stimuli.

4 Ears: vibrations in the air; eyes: light; nose and tongue: chemicals in solution; skin: changes in temperature, touch, pressure.

14 Insulin

1 Insulin regulates the blood-sugar level to 0.1g glucose per 100cm^3 blood. It helps to remove excess glucose from the blood by being involved in changing excess glucose to glycogen, which is stored in the liver, and increasing the rate that glucose is used in the body.

2 Controlling the diet so that carbohydrate intake is strictly regulated.

3 (a) Person P.

(b) These coincide with meal times.

15 Sex hormones

1 Testosterone.

2 Testes.

3 Puberty or adolescence.

4 Deepens the voice; enlarges the larynx; makes the body more muscular; causes sperm production; increases muscle development; causes facial, pubic, armpit, and chest hair to increase.

16 Kidneys and excretion

1 To reabsorb glucose and other useful substances.

2 Blood pressure caused by the heart.

3 (a) Protein and glucose.

(b) Protein has remained in the blood because the molecules are too big to pass through the filter. Glucose has been reabsorbed into the blood capillaries of the tubules.

(c) Filtration and reabsorption.

4 Filtration under pressure forces small molecules through the capillary wall and allows cells and large molecules to be retained.

17 Kidneys and regulation

1 8

2 When there is little water available to the animal, very little is absorbed into the blood stream. When blood contains little water it triggers the production of antidiuretic hormone from the pituitary gland in the brain. This circulates in the blood and when it reaches the kidneys it causes them to reabsorb as much water as possible.

The longer the tubule, the more surface area it has to do this.

3 The desert rat needs to conserve as much as possible.

18 Temperature regulation

1 1 = hair; 2 = sweat pore; 3 = sweat gland.

2 (a) Diameter becomes smaller.

(b) Diameter becomes larger.

3 Sweat is produced; hairs lie flat on the surface.

4 Heat is lost by latent heat of evaporation.

19 Photosynthesis

1 (a) Iodine.

(b) Turns black.

2 Plants use the carbon dioxide, produced by the fish, for photosynthesis which provide the fish with oxygen. The plants also provide food.

3 The conversion of light energy to chemical energy in food made by plants from carbon dioxide and water using chlorophyll.

4 Photosynthesis produces oxygen which reacts with the iron to produce rust.

20 Transpiration

1 Stomata.

2 Transpiration.

3a A: 3g, B: 0.5g, C: 0g.

b The lower.

21 Plant hormones

1 The seedlings in A would be strong and upright with green leaves. The seedlings in B would be long and weak with small yellow leaves well-spaced on the stem. The seedlings in C would have grown towards the light.

2 Gravity; roots grow downwards, stems grow in the opposite direction.

3 Hormones (auxins).

4 It causes stems and leaves to gow towards light for photosynthesis.

22 Natural selection

1 (c)

2 The industrial pollution altered the environment in which the moths lived. The dark-coloured forms already in the population were camouflaged from birds and so had a selective advantage and

survived to breed. They were better adapted to the new environmental conditions. Light-coloured moths were at a disadvantage and were reduced in numbers.

3 Since the *Clean Air Act* of 1956, less industrial pollution has occurred. The background on which the moths settled would no longer be blackened by soot, so the black moths would no longer be camouflaged. Reversal of the pre-1956 conditions would take place. The light-coloured moths would now be at an advantage and survive to breed, hence their numbers would increase and the numbers of the dark-coloured form would decrease.

23 Mutation

1 (a)

2 It was less well camouflaged so more easily seen by the birds that prey upon it.

3 The black form of snail would be at an advantage because it would now be difficult to see against the blackened background so its numbers would increase.

4 The radioactive fallout increased the mutation rate. A gene mutation resulted in a new form. The brown form, being well-camouflaged against the dark background, survived to breed and, as it was well-adapted to the environment, its numbers increased.

24 Gender determination

1 A = nucleus; B = chromosome.

2 (a) A = XX; B = XY.

(b) A = female; B = male.

25 Genetic crosses

1 Chromosomes.

2 (a) bb.

(b) Bb, BB.

3 (a) Bb and Bb.

(b) 50%.

26 Inherited diseases

1 A disorder which can be inherited because it is controlled by one or more mutated genes.

2 Mucus blocks the bronchioles so air cannot pass in and out.

3 Bacteria trapped in the mucus are killed by antibiotics.

4 (a) (i) Nn   (ii) Nn   (iii) nn.

(b) NN or Nn.

27 DNA (deoxyribonucleic acid)

1 (a) Double helix.

   (b) T with A and A with T.

2 Enzymes.

28 Genetic engineering

1 1 = (b); 2 = (a); 3 = (c).

2 Enzymes.

3 The production of large numbers of genetically identical cells.

4 There may be objections to killing animals to obtain hormones or there may be cultural objections to using products from pigs.

29 Food chains

1 (a) The oak tree.

   (b) Bark beetle or caterpillar or mouse or squirrel or earthworm.

   (c) Hawk or owl or blackbird.

2 Bark → beetle → blackbird → hawk.

3 (a) Mice would increase because there are fewer owls to eat them.

   (b) Squirrels would decrease because there would be more competition for their food from mice.

30 Concentration through food chains

Some of the insecticide has reached the pond by being washed in by rain. Some has been taken into the plants in the pond. When animals in the food chain feed on each other, the concentration of the insecticide builds up and eventually reaches a toxic level in the fish.

31 Food webs

1 Only plants can make food by photosynthesis.

2 Energy flow.

3 There would be a decrease in foxes and possibly an increase in those animals that eat grass because of less competition.

32 Food pyramids

1 The diagram should be a triangle with the following levels, starting at the base and moving upwards: plants; snails and worms; insects and leeches; small fish; large fish.

2 Large fish.

33 The carbon cycle

1 = Respiration by microbes.

2 = Burning of coal and oil.

3 = Photosynthesis.

4 = Decay.

5 = Feeding.

34 The nitrogen cycle

1 Protein.

2 Bacteria and fungi.

3 1, 2 and 5.

Chemistry

35 Atomic structure

1

Atom	Sodium	Aluminium	Fluorine
No. of protons	11	13	9
Number of neutrons	12	14	8
Number of electrons	11	13	9
Atomic number	11	13	9
Mass number	23	27	17

2 (a) 7p, 7n, 7e.

   (b) 5p, 6n, 5e.

   (c) 53p, 74n, 53e.

   (d) 15p, 16n, 15e.

   (e) 26p, 30n, 26e.

3 Because all atoms contain an equal number of positive protons and negative electrons.

4 The circulating negative electrons are held by attraction to the positive protons in the nucleus.

5 Isotopes are atoms of the same element which have the same number of protons (same atomic number) but different numbers of neutrons and hence different total masses (different mass numbers).

6 Similarities: each has 8 protons and 8 electrons.

Differences: the different isotopes have 8, 9 or 10 neutrons respectively.

36 Electrons in atoms

1 The arrangement of electrons in the shells or energy levels of an atom.

2 (a) 2.4

   (b) 2.6

   (c) 2.8.7

   (d) 2.8.8

3 (a) 11

   (b) 23

   (c) 11

   (d) 12

   (e) 2.8.1

4

5 Five electrons in the outer shell.

6 (a) 2.8.8.1

   (b) 2.8.8.2

   (c) 2.8.9.2

37 Ionic bonding

1 An atomic particle which has an electric charge due to the loss or gain of one or more electrons.

2 An ion with a single positive charge. The number of positive protons exceeds the number of negative electrons by one.

3 (a) K^+

   (b) Ca^{2+}

   (c) O^{2-}

   (d) Mg^{2+}

   (e) Br^-

4 (a)

(b)

(c)

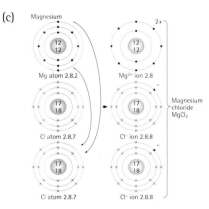

5 (a) Both have an electronic configuration of 2.8 but they have different numbers of protons and hence different charges. Sodium has 11 protons and so its ion is unipositive; the magnesium ion has 12 protons and so has two positive charges.

(b) Both have the same electronic configuration of 2.8 but they have different numbers of protons and hence different charges. The magnesium ion has 12 protons and so has two positive charges; the oxide ion has 8 protons and so has two negative charges.

38 Covalent bonding

1 A shared pair of electrons joining two atoms together. One electron from each atom makes up the pair.

2 A discrete particle made up of two or more atoms joined to each other by covalent bonds.

3 The forces between discrete, covalent molecules are very small and therefore the molecules are easy to separate from each other by heat energy. Hence covalent compounds have low melting and boiling points.

4 (a) Water (H_2O)

(b) Ammonia (NH_3)

(c) Chlorine (Cl_2)

5 Giant molecules have large numbers of atoms joined into a continuous structure by covalent bonds. The heat energy required to separate these is extremely high and hence melting points also high.

6 A bond consisting of two shared pairs of electrons. Each pair has one electron from each atom.

7 Ethene C_2H_4

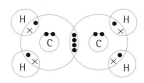

39 Reactivity and the extraction of metals

1 A list of metals arranged in order of reactivity, the most reactive at the top.

2 (a) Two of potassium, sodium, calcium, magnesium.

(b) Two of lead, copper, mercury, silver, gold.

3 (a) zinc + lead nitrate → zinc nitrate + lead

(b) lead + copper sulphate → lead sulphate + copper

(c) no reaction

(d) copper + silver nitrate → copper nitrate + silver

4 Lithium is a very reactive metal with compounds too stable to be reduced chemically.

5 Reactive metals have stable compounds which are difficult to reduce; unreactive metals have less stable compounds which are easier to reduce.

40 Extraction by reduction

1 A rock from which metals are obtained.

2 Four of zinc, iron, lead, copper, mercury.

3 Zinc blende (zinc sulphide).

The ore is roasted in air and the oxide obtained is reduced to zinc by heating with coke (carbon).

$2ZnS (s) + 3O^2 (g) \rightarrow 2ZnO (s) + 2SO^2 (g)$

$2ZnO (s) + C (s) \rightarrow 2Zn (s) + CO^2 (g)$

4 Zinc is more reactive than mercury and therefore its compounds are more stable. The oxide of zinc will not decompose on heating whereas the oxide of mercury will.

5 $2PbO (s) + C (s) \rightarrow 2Pb (s) + CO^2 (g)$

lead oxide + carbon → lead + carbon dioxide

41 Extraction by electrolysis

1 In molten sodium chloride the ions are free to move from place to place; in solid sodium chloride the ions are fixed in place.

2 Sodium ion, Na^+; chloride ion, Cl^-.

3 The ions present are Na^+ and Cl^-. The Na^+ ions are attracted to the negative cathode where they gain electrons to become sodium atoms:

$2Na^+ + 2e^- \rightarrow 2Na (s)$

The chloride ions are attracted to the positive anode where they give up electrons to form chlorine molecules:

$2Cl^- - 2e^- \rightarrow Cl_2 (g)$

Overall the reaction is:

$2NaCl (l) \rightarrow 2Na (s) + Cl_2 (g)$

4 Blister copper is the impure copper extracted from the ore copper pyrites by heating the ore in air. The copper pyrites is reduced to copper.

$Cu_2S (s) + O_2 (g) \rightarrow 2Cu (s) + SO_2 (g)$

5 The blister copper is purified by making it the anode of a cell in which the cathode is pure copper and the electrolyte is copper sulphate solution. The ions present are Cu^{2+} and SO_4^{2-}. At the positive anode the Cu atoms of the anode each give up two electrons:

$Cu (s) \rightarrow Cu^{2+} (aq) + 2e^-$

The Cu2+ (aq) ions are attracted to the negative cathode where they gain two electrons each:

$Cu^{2+} (aq) + 2e^- \rightarrow Cu (s)$

Thus the process results in the copper dissolving from the anode and pure copper being deposited onto the cathode.

6 (a) The ions present are K^+ and Cl^-. The electrolysis proceeds exactly as in question 3, substituting K^+ for Na^+ and K for Na in the equations.

(b) The ions present are Al^{3+} and O^{2-}. At the anode the oxide ions each give up two electrons to form oxygen molecules:

$2O^{2-} - 4e^- \rightarrow O_2$

At the cathode the aluminium ions each gain three electrons to form aluminium.

$Al^{3+} + 3e^- \rightarrow Al$

The overall reaction is:

$2Al_2O_3 (l) \rightarrow 4Al (s) + 3O_2 (g)$

7 The forces between the multi-charged Al^{3+} and O^{2-} ions of the aluminium oxide are approximately three times greater than the forces between the uni-charged Na^+ and Cl^- ions of the sodium chloride.

42 Organic chemistry

1 The study of carbon compounds.

2 A compound containing only carbon and hydrogen.

3 The ability to use covalent bonding to form long chains.

4 (a)

$$H-\underset{\underset{H}{|}}{\overset{\overset{H}{|}}{C}}-\underset{\underset{H}{|}}{\overset{\overset{H}{|}}{C}}-\underset{\underset{H}{|}}{\overset{\overset{H}{|}}{C}}-H$$

(b)

$$H-\underset{\underset{H}{|}}{\overset{\overset{H}{|}}{C}}-H$$

(c)

$$\underset{H}{\overset{H}{\diagdown}}C=C\underset{\diagdown H}{\overset{\diagup H}{}}$$

(d)

$$H-\underset{\underset{H}{|}}{\overset{\overset{H}{|}}{C}}-\underset{\underset{H}{|}}{\overset{\overset{H}{|}}{C}}=C\underset{\diagdown H}{\overset{\diagup H}{}}$$

5 (a) A compound containing only single bonds.

   (b) A compound containing only double bonds.

6 (a) ethanol C_2H_5OH

$$\underset{H}{\overset{H}{\diagdown}}H-\underset{\underset{H}{|}}{\overset{\overset{H}{|}}{C}}-C-O-H$$

   (b) ethanamine $C_2H_5NH_2$

$$\underset{H}{\overset{H}{\diagdown}}H-\underset{\underset{H}{|}}{\overset{\overset{H}{|}}{C}}-\underset{\underset{H}{|}}{\overset{\overset{H}{|}}{C}}-N$$

7 (a) CH_3OH.

   (b) C_3H_7Cl.

   (c) CH_3NH_2.

43 Fractional distillation

1 Because it has been formed over millions of years from plant and animal remains.

2 Heating crude oil to separate it into its different components by means of their different boiling points.

3 Any three of the fractions from the table in the text, together with the appropriate information.

4 (a) $CH_4 + 2O_2 \rightarrow 2H_2O + CO_2$

   (b) $2C_4H_{10} + 13O_2 \rightarrow 10H_2O + 8CO_2$

   (c) $2C_{10}H_{22} + 31O_2 \rightarrow 22H_2O + 20CO_2$

44 Polymerisation

1 Breaking long hydrocarbons down into smaller molecules using high temperatures and, usually, a catalyst.

2 The short chain molecules are more useful and in greater demand than the long chain molecules.

3 Because they are unsaturated hydrocarbons. The double bond can be broken and the carbon atoms can join together to form long chains.

4 The making of polymers – long chain molecules of thousands of carbon atoms – from monomers – small single molecules with a double bond. The monomers join together when heated under pressure in the presence of a catalyst. An example is polythene.

5

$$\cdots\cdots\underset{\underset{H}{|}}{\overset{\overset{H}{|}}{C}}-\underset{\underset{Cl}{|}}{\overset{\overset{H}{|}}{C}}-\underset{\underset{H}{|}}{\overset{\overset{H}{|}}{C}}-\underset{\underset{Cl}{|}}{\overset{\overset{H}{|}}{C}}-\underset{\underset{H}{|}}{\overset{\overset{H}{|}}{C}}-\underset{\underset{Cl}{|}}{\overset{\overset{H}{|}}{C}}-\underset{\underset{H}{|}}{\overset{\overset{H}{|}}{C}}-\underset{\underset{Cl}{|}}{\overset{\overset{H}{|}}{C}}\cdots\cdots$$

(The number of C atoms shown in the section is not important but each alternate C atom should have a Cl atom attached.)

45 Products from air

1 Nitrogen, oxygen and carbon dioxide.

2 78% nitrogen, 21% oxygen.

3 Ammonia.

4 The air.

5 N_2 (g) + $3H_2$ (g) $\underset{\substack{500-550°C \\ \text{Fe catalyst}}}{\overset{250 \text{ atmospheres}}{\rightleftharpoons}}$ $2NH_3$ (g) + heat

6 An artificial fertiliser containing nitrogen.

7 $2NH_3$ (g) + H_2SO_4 (aq) $\rightarrow$ $(NH_4)_2SO_4$ (aq)

   NH_3 (g) + HNO_3 (aq) $\rightarrow$ NH_4NO_3 (aq)

8 Nitrogen is required to make proteins for healthy growth.

9 By taking nitrogen compounds from the soil and converting them to protein.

10 Fertilisers are needed to replace the nutrients in soil as they are depleted by continuous use of the soil.

11 Fertilisers produce high yields of healthy crops and do this quickly.

12 Rain washes fertilisers into rivers, streams and lakes. The fertilisers cause algae and bacteria to grow in the water. These use oxygen and reduce light levels causing fish to die.

13 Fertilisers get washed into reservoirs by rain and hence into drinking water.

14 They do not occur naturally, they are manufactured.

46 The atmosphere and the oceans

1 When plant life formed it began to photosynthesise, using the carbon dioxide in the atmosphere and producing oxygen.

2 Oxygen levels increased steadily as more and more plants appeared on the Earth and produced oxygen by photosynthesis. When animal life appeared the oxygen was used for respiration and levels fell. Eventually a balance was reached between the production of oxygen by photosynthesis and its use in respiration so that the level remained stable.

3 The seas were at first pure, condensed water but then minerals from the Earth's crust and gases from the atmosphere dissolved in the water.

4 As forests are cleared there are fewer plants to use carbon dioxide in photosynthesis. Thus carbon dioxide levels increase and add to the greenhouse effect.

5 There are a number of possible effects of global warming. Suggestions include melting ice caps leading to rising sea levels; evaporation of surface water causing increasing areas of desert; disturbed weather patterns across the globe which meteorologists do not yet understand and cannot predict; effects on plant life as both soil and atmospheric conditions change.

47 Natural cycles: the carbon cycle

1 Materials are continually produced and used up but a balance is maintained by recycling.

2 Three of, for example, carbon, nitrogen, water, rock.

3 Atmospheric carbon dioxide is taken in by plants during photosynthesis. Animals eat these plants. When plants and animals die the carbon returns to the soil via the decomposed remains.

4 Carbon is returned to the atmosphere by the respiration of plants and

animals, the bacterial decay of plant and animal remains and the burning of fossil fuels. (Only two of these required by the question.)

5   Burning fossil fuels puts CO_2 into the atmosphere. This is heavy and remains in the atmosphere.

    It then traps heat in and adds to the Greenhouse Effect.

48 Rocks

1   The first rocks on the Earth were formed by the cooling and solidification of molten rock (magma). This always produces igneous rock and not other types.

2   (a) Igneous.

    (b) Igneous rock is formed by the cooling and solidification of molten rock (magma). Basalt has small crystals because it was formed by rapid cooling and granite has large crystals because it was formed by slow cooling.

3   The breaking up of rocks by freezing and thawing, heating and cooling, root growth or attack by chemicals in air, rain or soil.

4   The removal of rock fragments by the impact of wind, water, rocks or animals, including humans.

5   Rock fragments, called sediment, are removed by erosion. The sediment is deposited in quieter conditions. Over millions of years the layers of sediment can build up and the lower, older layers are compacted and cemented together into sedimentary rocks.

6   The study of how sediments are formed, how volcanoes erupt and the effects of earthquakes today; the observation of rock features; the study of shock waves travelling through the Earth after an earthquake.

7   Dead plants and animals are trapped in the layers of sedimentary rocks. The fossils in the lower layers will be older than those in the more recently-deposited upper layers.

49 Balanced chemical equations

1   (a) $Zn + 2HCl \rightarrow ZnCl_2 + H_2$

    (b) $C + CO_2 \rightarrow 2CO$

    (c) $2H_2 + O_2 \rightarrow 2H_2O$

    (d) $2Al + Fe_2O_3 \rightarrow Al_2O_3 + 2Fe$

    (e) $2KOH + H_2SO_4 \rightarrow K_2SO_4 + 2H_2O$

    (f) $ZnSO_4 + 2NaOH \rightarrow Zn(OH)_2 + Na_2SO_4$

    (g) $2Pb(NO_3)_2 \rightarrow 2PbO + 4NO_2 + O_2$

2   (a) $CuO + H_2 \rightarrow Cu + H_2O$

    (b) $2Na + 2H_2O \rightarrow 2NaOH + H_2$

    (c) $N_2 + 3H_2 \rightleftharpoons 2NH_3$

    (d) $ZnCO_3 \rightarrow ZnO + CO_2$

    (e) $2NaOH + MgCl_2 \rightarrow Mg(OH)_2 + 2NaCl$

50 Reacting masses

1   5.6g.

2   8g of oxygen are required; 9g of water are produced.

3   6.2g.

4   0.46g.

51 Determining formulae

1   $4 \div 1 = 4$ moles of hydrogen react with $32 \div 16 = 2$ moles of oxygen.

    The ratio is 2:1 so the formula of water is H_2O.

2   $2 \div 1 = 2$ moles of hydrogen react with $32 \div 32 = 1$ mole of sulphur.

    The ratio is 2:1 so the formula of hydrogen sulphide is H_2S.

3   $6 \div 12 = 0.5$ moles of carbon react with $16 \div 16 = 1$ mole of oxygen.

    The ratio is 1:2 so the formula of carbon dioxide is CO_2.

4   Mass of chlorine = (11.7 - 4.6)g = 7.1g.

    So $4.6 \div 23 = 0.2$ moles of sodium react with $7.1 \div 35.5 = 0.2$ moles of chlorine.

    The ratio is 1:1 so the formula of sodium chloride is NaCl.

5   Mass of oxygen = (4 - 3.2)g = 0.8g.

    So $3.2 \div 64 = 0.05$ moles of copper react with $0.8 \div 16 = 0.05$ moles of oxygen.

    The ratio is 1:1 so the formula of copper oxide is CuO.

52 Introducing the periodic table

1   A table containing all the elements listed in order of their atomic number, beginning with hydrogen, atomic number 1.

2   A vertical column of elements having the same number of electrons in the outer shell. The group number is the same as the number of electrons in the outer shell.

3   Elements in a group have the same as the number of electrons in the outer shell and have similar chemical properties.

4   A horizontal row of elements with the same configuration of electrons in their inner shell(s) but with increasing numbers of electrons in the outermost shell as you move from left to right across the period.

5   Elements in a period have the same configuration of electrons in their inner shell(s).

6   The transition metals are those elements that fit in the periodic table between group II and group III.

53 Properties of elements

1   (a) Any two elements in group I, other than sodium.

    (b) Any two elements in group II, other than calcium.

    (c) Any two elements in group VI, other than sulphur.

    (d) Any two elements in group VII, other than fluorine.

2   (a) The bottom element in group I.

    (b) The top element in group VII.

    (c) Period 3, sodium to argon.

    (d) Group VI.

3   (a) Three of A, D, E, F; D is the most metallic.

    (b) B and C; B is the most non-metallic.

    (c) (i) D_2B (ii)   AB

    (d) They are transition metals.

    (e) No; they are both metals and metals do not form compounds with each other.

54 Noble gases

1   The atoms get heavier and so the inter-atomic forces become greater.

2   Because they do not undergo any chemical reactions as they already have complete outer electron shells.

3   The atoms existing singly. Atoms of the noble gases have complete outer shells and hence do not join to each other; they remain as individual atoms.

4   It is lighter than air and non-flammable.

5   Its inertness prevents the filament from burning away.

55 Alkali metals

1 They all have a single electron in the outer shell.

2 The one outer electron is easier to lose as it gets further away from the positive nucleus and is, therefore, less strongly held.

3 (a) KCl

   (b) Na_2O

   (c) LiOH

4 (a) $2Na + Br_2 \rightarrow 2NaBr$

      sodium bromide

   (b) $4K + O_2 \rightarrow 2K_2O$

      potassium oxide

   (c) $2Na + 2H_2O \rightarrow 2NaOH + H_2$

      sodium hydroxide and hydrogen

56 Alkali metal compounds

1 There is no reaction. Sodium is a very reactive metal and its compounds are stable to heat.

2 Potassium is a very reactive metal and its compounds are very stable. Electrolysis is therefore necessary. Molten potassium chloride is the electrolyte. Potassium is deposited at the anode and chlorine gas given off at the cathode.

    $2KCl\ (l) \rightarrow 2K\ (s) + Cl_2\ (g)$

3 (a) sodium carbonate

   (b) sodium hydroxide

   (c) sodium hydroxide

   (d) sodium chloride

   (e) sodium chloride

   (f) sodium hydroxide

   (g) sodium chloride

   (h) sodium chloride

4 (a) $2K^+; O2^-$

   (b) $Li^+; OH^-$

   (c) $2Na^+; CO_3{}^{2-}$

   (d) $2K^+; SO_4{}^{2-}$

   (e) $Na^+; NO3^-$

   (f) $K^+; Br^-$

57 Halogens

1 (a) Dark brown or black.

   (b) Solid.

   (c) About 250°C.

2 (a) $2Na + I_2 \rightarrow 2NaI$

      sodium iodide

   (b) $Br_2 + H_2 \rightarrow 2HBr$

      hydrogen bromide

3 Chlorine is reacted with hydrogen to form hydrogen chloride gas:

    $Cl_2\ (g) + H_2\ (g) \rightarrow 2HCl\ (g)$

   The hydrogen chloride gas is then dissolved in water to form hydrochloric acid:

    $HCl\ (g) + H2O \rightarrow HCl\ (aq)$

4 Iodine: between 90°C and 130°C.

   Astatine: between 150°C and 200°C.

58 Halogen compounds

1 (a) $Cl_2 + 2NaBr \rightarrow 2NaCl + Br_2$

   (b) No reaction.

   (c) $Br_2 + 2NaI \rightarrow 2NaBr + I_2$

   (d) No reaction.

2 (a) $Ca^{2+}; 2Cl^-$

   (b) $Na^+; I^-$

   (c) $Mg^{2+}; 2Br^-$

   (d) $Li^+; Cl^-$

3 (a)

   (b)

   (c)

   (d)

59 Transition metals

1 (a) The spaces in the incomplete shell allows the movement of electrons.

   (b) The strong inter-atomic forces mean that high energy levels are required for melting to occur.

   (c) The same number of electron shells are in use across the series.

   (d) They all have similar electronic configurations, i.e. two electrons in the outermost (fourth) shell and an incomplete third shell (except zinc).

   (e) They all lose electrons to form positive ions during reaction.

2 Zinc has complete inner shells as the non-transition metals do.

3 If the tin plating is cracked and the iron exposed then the iron will react in preference to the tin and thus the protection is lost. If the zinc plating used in galvanising is cracked and the iron exposed then the zinc will react in preference to the iron so the protection is maintained.

4 Zinc has complete inner shells of electrons so the inter-atomic forces are lower in zinc than in the other transition metals. Hence the melting point is lower.

60 Oxidation

1 The gain of oxygen or the loss of hydrogen.

2 A provider of oxygen or a remover of hydrogen.

3 (a) Oxidised: carbon (C); oxidising agent: zinc oxide (ZnO)

   (b) Oxidised: carbon monoxide (CO); oxidising agent: iron oxide (Fe_2O_3)

   (c) Oxidised: sulphur (S); oxidising agent: oxygen (O_2)

   (d) Oxidised: hydrogen bromide (HBr); oxidising agent: chlorine (Cl_2)

   (e) Oxidised: methane (CH_4); oxidising agent: chlorine (Cl_2).

4 (a) The sodium gains oxygen or loses electrons:

      $Na - e^- \rightarrow Na^+$

   (b) The calcium loses electrons:

      $Ca - 2e^- \rightarrow Ca^{2+}$

   (c) The sodium loses electrons:

      $Na - e^- \rightarrow Na^+$

   (d) The iron loses electrons:

      $Fe - 2e^- \rightarrow Fe^{2+}$

61 Reduction and redox reactions

1 Loss of oxygen, gain of hydrogen or gain of electrons.

2 (a) Reduced: copper oxide (CuO); reducing agent: carbon (C)

   (b) Reduced: bromine (Br_2); reducing agent: hydrogen sulphide (H_2S)

   (c) Reduced: chlorine (Cl2); reducing agent: lithium (Li).

3 (a) aluminium (Al)

   (b) iron oxide (Fe_2O_3)

   (c) iron oxide (Fe_2O_3)

   (d) aluminium (Al)

4 A reaction in which oxidation and reduction occur together.

5   The bromide ions (Br^-) are oxidised and the chlorine molecule (Cl_2) is reduced.

$$Cl_2 + 2e^- \rightarrow 2Cl^-$$
$$2Br^- - 2e^- \rightarrow Br^2$$

6   When calcium burns in air, calcium oxide is formed.

$$2Ca\,(s) + O2\,(g) \rightarrow 2CaO\,(s)$$

The calcium atoms lose 2 electrons each and thus calcium is oxidised.

$$2Ca - 4e^- \rightarrow 2Ca^{2+} \text{ oxidation}$$

The atoms in the oxygen molecule gain 2 electrons each and thus oxygen is reduced.

$$O_2 + 4e^- \rightarrow 2O^{2-} \text{ reduction}$$

62 Neutralisation

1   (a) A solution with pH lower than 7.
    (b) A solution with pH greater than 7.

2   The reaction between an acid and an alkali. The product is neutral (pH = 7).

3   (a) $H_2SO_4 + 2KOH \rightarrow K_2SO_4 + 2H_2O$
    (b) $H^+ + OH^- \rightarrow H_2O$

4   (a) $HCl + KOH \rightarrow KCl + H_2O$
    (b) $H^+ + OH^- \rightarrow H_2O$

5   Dilute sulphuric acid conducts electricity well and so must contain many ions. Concentrated sulphuric acid is a poor conductor and so must contain few ions. The ionisation of sulphuric acid increases with dilution.

63 Thermal decomposition

1   The breaking down of a compound.

2   The breaking down of a compound by heat.

3   $MgCO_3 \rightarrow MgO + CO_2$
    Magnesium oxide and carbon dioxide.

4   Sodium is a very reactive metal and hence its compounds are stable to heat.

5   (a) Potassium is a reactive metal.
    (b) By electrolysis: $2KCl \rightarrow 2K + Cl_2$

64 Enzymes

1   Enzymes are proteins found in the human body.

2   They catalyse the chemical reactions in the body.

3   They work by fitting into the reactant molecule like a jigsaw piece. Each enzyme catalyses only one particular reaction.

4   Two of, for example, amylase, lysozyme, protease, pysozyme.

5   A biological washing powder works by chemical reactions similar to those occurring in the body. It contains enzymes called proteases which break down the proteins in the substances which stain clothes, such as oil and blood.

65 Patterns and predictions

1   (a) zinc + oxygen → zinc oxide
        $$2Zn + O_2 \rightarrow 2ZnO$$
    (b) copper oxide + hydrogen → copper + water
        $$CuO + H_2 \rightarrow Cu + H_2O$$

2   (a) 2.6
    (b) Group VI.
    (c) Non-metal.
    (d) Yes; Y2–.
    (e) Yes; covalent; two non-metals always form covalent compounds.

3   (a) magnesium + zinc sulphate → magnesium sulphate + zinc
    (b) No reaction.
    (c) zinc + copper sulphate → zinc sulphate + copper
    (d) No reaction.

66 Rates of reaction

1   (a) For example: burning, precipitation, acids on carbonates.
    (b) For example: cooking, decomposition (rotting) of food.

2   A collision between particles that have enough energy to cause reaction (activation energy) rather than just bounce away from each other.

3   (a) Rate increases with increasing concentration because increasing the number of particles increases the number of fruitful collisions.
    (b) Lowering the temperature decreases the rate because molecules have less energy and hence there are fewer fruitful collisions.
    (c) Larger pieces of marble chip mean that a smaller surface area of marble is exposed to the acid. Reducing the number of particles exposed reduces the rate.
    (d) Catalysts reduce the activation energy required for a fruitful collision.

4   Inhibitors work by increasing the activation energy required for a fruitful collision.

67 Energy transfers in chemical reactions

1   (a) Methane and oxygen.
    (b)

    (c) DH is negative because the change in heat content is a downwards one, i.e. a negative one.

2   (a) One N—N bond and three H—H bonds.
    (b) Six N—H bonds.
    (c) If DH is negative the reaction is exothermic. Hence the energy contained in the six N—H bonds is lower than the energy in the one N—N and three H—H bonds.

3   (a) DH = 436 + 224 + 2(–366) = –72 kJ/mole
    (b) Exothermic.

68 Reversible reactions: the Haber process

1   A reaction in which both forward and backward reactions take place simultaneously.

2   The point at which forward and backward reactions take place at the same rate.

3   The amounts of reactants and products present at equilibrium.

4   The equilibrium will move to the right. The reaction is exothermic and hence by moving to the right produces more heat to replace the heat lost by the temperature decrease.

5   (a) The system will try to absorb the increased heat and, as the reaction is exothermic, the position of equilibrium will move towards the left.
    (b) Increasing container size allows the system to expand and hence move to the side with more molecules. The position of equilibrium moves towards the left.
    (c) No effect on the position of equilibrium.
    (d) It moves from left to right to replace the removed ammonia.
    (e) It moves from right to left to replace the removed nitrogen.

Physics

69 Electric current and voltage

1

2 A: 0.2A; B: 0.5A.

3 (a) 0.5A.

   (b) 6V.

70 Resistance

1 voltage (volts) = current (amps) x resistance (Ω).

2 10 V.

3 (a)

   (b) When the current in the circuit increases, more charge per second passes through the lamp. More energy per second is delivered by the current so the lamp glows more brightly.

4 48 Ω.

71 Components in circuits

1 As the current in the lamp increases, more energy is delivered to the lamp, so the temperature increases and so the resistance increases.

2 A diode only allows current to flow in one direction. Between -5 V and 0 V the voltage is negative and no current flows. As the voltage across the diode increases from 0 V to +5 V the current increases.

3 (a) As the light shining on an LDR gets brighter the resistance of the LDR decreases.

   (b) As the resistance of the LDR decreases, more current can flow in the circuit.

72 Electrical power and energy

1 (a) 36 W.

   (b) 10 800 J.

   (c) 4 Ω.

2 (a) 2000 W.

   (b) 120 000 J.

   (c) 8.7 A.

73 Electricity at home

1 0.25 kW.

2 (a) 6 kWh.

   (b) 48 pence.

3 A fuse is designed to melt when the current in the circuit becomes too large. The fuse melts and breaks the circuit before other wires in the circuit overheat and cause a fire.

4 The earth wire is normally to the metal casing of an appliance to prevent the user getting a shock. Double insulated appliances do not have metal exposed to the user.

5 (a) 10 A.

   (b) 13 A. The other fuses would melt when the normal operating current passes through the circuit.

74 Electric charge

1 (a) Negative.

   (b) Positive.

   (c)

   The balloons have the same charge so will repel each other and move apart.

2 A jumper brushing against hair will transfer electrons from the jumper to the hair. The electrons make the hair negatively charged, so the individual hairs will repel each other, all trying to get as far apart as possible.

3 (a) 900 C.

   (b) 10 800 J.

   (c) 12 J.

   (d) 12 V.

75 Electric charge – good and bad

1 Walking across a carpet transfers charge from the carpet to your body. When you touch a door handle (a good conductor) some of the charge crosses from your hand to the handle; the current is felt as an electric shock.

2 The television screen becomes charged by the stream of electrons which cause the picture to form. The charge on the screen attracts dust particles.

3 The charged balloon attracts opposite charges in the wall, causing the two to stick together.

76 Electric motors

1 To make the force on the wires bigger and the motor spin faster you can make the current bigger; or have more turns on the coil or use stronger magnets.

   To make the force move the wire in the opposite direction you can reverse the current or reverse the magnetic field.

2

When the current is from A to B in one side of the coil it is from C to D in the other side of the coil. So AB moves up whilst CD moves down. When the coil is vertical there are no contacts so there is no current and the coil keeps turning. When side AB reaches the right-hand side the current is now in the opposite direction in the magnetic field so the wire moves down, CD moves up and the coil continues to spin.

77 Electromagnetic induction and transformers

1 (a) The needle remains at zero (no induced voltage).

   (b) The needle flicks to the left (induced voltage in the opposite direction).

   (c) The needle flicks to the left (induced voltage in the opposite direction).

   (d) The needle flicks to the right.

   (e) The needle flicks to the right.

2 A voltage can only be induced in the secondary coil when there is a changing magnetic field in the iron core. The changing current in the primary coil produces the changing

magnetic field. A direct current would produce a steady magnetic field and so no induced voltage.

3   IO V.

78 From power station to customer

1   The spinning magnet provides a magnetic field which passes through the coil. The movement of the magnet makes a constantly changing magnetic field through the coils.

2   Transformers need an alternating current to produce the changing magnetic field required to induce a voltage in the secondary coil. This is achieved by generating alternating current which then results in an a.c. output from the secondary coil.

3   Fossil fuels are a limited resource which will eventually be used up; fossil fuels are also used to make materials not easily made in other ways; burning fossil fuels increases air pollution; burning fossil fuels increases the carbon dioxide in the atmosphere, which contributes to global warming.

4   Not all the energy from the coal will heat the boiler – some transferred to the surroundings. Some energy from the hot pipes warms the atmosphere. Energy is lost to the surroundings from the cooling towers. Energy is lost because the transmission cables become warm as the energy passes through them. Energy is lost in the transformers – they become warm and sometimes 'hum'.

5   (a)   8000 A.
    (b)   500 A.

79 Distance and speed

1   25 m/s.

2   (a)   13.3 m/s.
    (b)   The cyclist was stationary.
    (c)   10 m/s.
    (d)   The cyclist turned round and went back towards the origin at 10 m/s.

80 Acceleration

1   5 m/s^2

2   During the first 10 s the bus accelerates from 0 m/s^2 to 10 m/s^2. Between 10 s and 30 s it travels at a steady speed of 10 m/s. From 30 s to 40 s it accelerates from 10 m/s to 15 m/s and then travels at a steady speed of 15 m/s for 10 s. It slows down from 15 m/s to 5 m/s in 10 s.

3   8 m/s^2.

4   20 m/s.

81 Forces and motion

1   Parachutist: forces balanced so falling at a steady speed
    Cyclist: force backwards greater so decelerating
    Car: forward force greater so accelerating

2   (a)   2 m/s^2.
    (b)   3000 N.

3   40 N.

4   36 000 N

82 Stopping a car

1   15 m.

2   The thinking distance would be longer because the driver would take longer to realise he needs to brake and would therefore travel further.

3   79 m.

4   A wet road would reduce friction so the braking distance would be longer and the overall stopping distance would be longer.

5   The stopping force would be greater because the stopping time would be shorter so the deceleration would be greater.

6   The tyres would make the stopping distance and stopping time longer than for the bollard and so the stopping force would be reduced.

83 Falling objects

1   A falling object is pulled towards the Earth by gravity. This force is called the weight of the object. An object falling through air will experience air resistance. Air resistance depends on the shape of the object and its speed. When the air resistance is equal to the weight of the object the object will stop accelerating and will move at a steady speed, called its terminal velocity.

2   (a)   Initially the parachutist falls at a low speed but accelerates rapidly. When the canopy opens the air resistance increases and so her acceleration is less. As she speeds up her air resistance increases until it balances her weight. She then falls at a steady speed, her terminal velocity.

   (b)   If the parachutist weighed less, she would need less air resistance to balance her weight, so her terminal velocity would have a lower value.

84 Waves

1   Echoes are due to sound reflected from a hard surface.

2   Refraction can be seen when a ruler is put in water. The ruler appears bent because the light has changed direction as it leaves the water.

3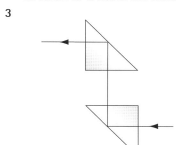

85 Waves 2

1   Longitudinal waves: sound waves.
    Transverse waves: light waves, water waves, waves along a rope.

2   Put a cork in some water. Drop a stone into the water. The waves travel out from the centre, making the cork floating on the water move up and down. Although circular waves travel out across the water, the water only moves up and down, and the cork does not move outwards.

3   330 m/s.

86 Sound and ultrasound

1   Sound travels by vibration being passed from one particle to the next. A vacuum does not contain any particles so there can be no transmission of sound.

2   50 Hz.

3   300 m/s.

4   For example, when you are in the hall you can hear the television, even though you cannot see it. The sound waves are diffracted through the open door. (If the door is closed the sound is much quieter, because it had to pass through the door.)

87 The electromagnetic spectrum

1   X-rays are an ionising radiation and are known to damage living cells; there is

no evidence that ultrasound damages cells.

2 Ultraviolet light from the Sun damages cells, which may lead to skin cancer.

3 Infrared is detected by the camera cells, the camera then converts it to an electrical signal and displays it in the visible spectrum.

4 Mobile phones emit microwaves; the phone is held close to the head. Other wavelengths of microwave are used in cooking.

88 Communications

1 Optical fibres are cheaper to make; optical fibres can carry many more signals in the same thickness cable; optical signals need boosting less often.

2 Microwaves can carry much more information and the ground does not have to be dug up to bury cables.

3 Digital signals suffer less from interference and the cables carrying digital signals can carry more information.

4 Diffraction.

89 Plate tectonics

1 (a) There may be volcanoes or earthquakes.

(b) Molten rock rises to the surface forming new plate material.

2 The coastlines of Africa and South America match in shape and the rocks and the fossil records suggest that they were once close together. When new plate material forms it records the direction of the Earth's magnetic field at that time. The patterns give information about the way the plates have formed.

90 Waves through the Earth

1 P waves are longitudinal waves, travel more quickly and can travel through solids, liquids and gases and, therefore, right through the Earth.

S waves are transverse waves, travel more slowly and can only pass through solids. They are not transmitted by the outer core of the Earth.

2 P waves travel more quickly than S waves, so there is a spread of time over which waves arrive. The further the station is from the epicentre the longer the time delay. The delay will be

longest at a position opposite the epicentre.

91 The Earth and beyond

1 (a) Venus.

(b) A.

(c) The path of a comet is a more stretched ellipse, passing way beyond the orbit of planet C.

(d) The comet moves fastest when it is closest to the Sun.

2 The Moon.

3 Gravity.

92 Our place in the universe

1 Stars are formed when gravity pulls together massive clouds of dust and gas in space, fusing hydrogen nuclei to make helium.

2 The Sun may expand to form a red giant and then contract to a white dwarf.

3 The dust and gases from a supernova may be attracted back together by gravity to eventually form a new star.

93 Energy and work

1 1250 J.

2 (a) 1200 N.

(b) 1800 J.

3 (a) 400 000 J.

(b) 400 kJ.

94 Power and efficiency

1 (a) 1600 J.

(b) 160 W.

(c) The lift would also need to lift the chair; the lift also has to overcome friction; the lift is not 100% efficient.

2 (a) 600 N.

(b) 20 m.

(c) 12 000 J.

(d) 67 W.

95 Potential energy and kinetic energy

1 Aircraft has kinetic energy and gravitational potential energy, both transferred by the engines from the fuel.

The cyclist has kinetic energy transferred from food.

The book on the shelf has gravitational potential energy transferred by the

person who placed it there from food.

2 (a) 0.5 kg.

(b) 5 N.

(c) 6 J.

(d) 1200 J.

(e) 6.7 W.

96 Energy transfers and temperature

1 The pan handle is a good insulator. It prevents the hand being burnt when removing the pan from the stove.

The coat is a good insulator. It prevents heat from the child's body escaping, making her cold.

The tank jacket is a good insulator. It prevents heat escaping from the hot tank.

The base of the pan is a good conductor. It allows the efficient transmission of heat.

2 (a) Energy is lost by conduction through poor insulation in roofs; energy is lost by conduction through single-glazed windows; energy is lost through draughts, cold air gets in under poorly fitting doors.

(b) Add loft insulation; double- or even triple-glazed windows; fit draught excluders.

97 Energy resources

1 Much of the energy has heated the engine and consequently the surroundings; some is used to overcome air resistance, again warming the air around the car; some warmed the road and tyres through friction; some warmed the brakes; eventually all the energy has warmed the surroundings.

2 Only 35% of the energy available from the coal was used to generate electricity.

3 Wind generators use a renewable energy resource but only work when the wind blows.

Water can be used to drive turbines, it does not pollute but the water supply needs replenishing by rain.

4 (a) A bus can carry fifty people in the road space of three cars, which might carry twelve people. The bus will use less fuel and cause less pollution than the three or more cars it replaces.

(b) Less traffic congestion; less air pollution

(c) Public transport does not take you door-to-door; it is not as reliable or as convenient as private transport.

98 Radioactivity

1 Charge.

2 Gamma rays; electromagnetic radiation can pass through a vacuum.

3 Two protons and two neutrons.

4 Gamma radiation has a much longer range in air.

5 Alpha radiation would be completely stopped by air; gamma radiation would pass through the paper almost unchanged, but the amount of beta radiation detected would depend on the thickness of the paper.

99 Half-life

1 (a) 6 hours.

   (b) Yes.

2 The long half-life means that the uranium-235 will have decayed since the rocks were formed but there will be some left.

100 Uses of radiation

1 (a) Neither alpha radiation nor beta radiation would penetrate to the site of the tumour.

   (b) Stops one part of the healthy body being over-exposed to radiation; allows the tumour to be treated from all sides.

2 The blood carries the iodine to the thyroid where it can work directly; beta radiation would not penetrate the body to reach the thyroid from outside.

Glossary

acceleration Acceleration tells us the rate at which a moving object is speeding up or slowing down. Acceleration is measured in metres / second² (m/s²).

acid Acids are substances which produce hydrogen **ions** when added to water. Acids have a **pH** below 7.

ADH ADH is antidiuretic **hormone** which controls the production of urine in the kidneys.

aerobic respiration During aerobic **respiration** oxygen is used in the process of transferring energy from glucose in the cells of the body.

alkali metals The alkali metals are the elements in group I of the **periodic table**. They have one electron in the outer **shell**.

alkalis Alkalis are substances which form hydroxide **ions** when added to water. Alkalis have a **pH** greater than 7.

alkenes Alkenes are unsaturated hydrocarbons with a double bond between the carbon atoms.

allele An allele is one version of the **gene** coding for a particular characteristic.

alternating current Alternating current (a.c.) is an **electric current** which regularly changes size and direction.

amp **Electric current** is measured in amps. 1 amp = 1 coulomb / second.

amplitude Amplitude is the distance from the crest of a wave to the place where there is no displacement.

anaerobic respiration During anaerobic **respiration** energy is transferred from glucose without oxygen.

analogue signals An analogue signal carries information by copying the changing pattern of the waves in the original information.

angle of incidence The angle of incidence is the angle between the direction of a wave and the **normal**.

artery An artery is a blood vessel with a thick muscular wall and a narrow space inside.

atom All **elements** are made of atoms. An atom consists of a **nucleus** containing **protons** and **neutrons** surrounded by **electrons**.

atomic number The atomic number (Z) of an **element** is the number of **protons** in the **nucleus of the atom**.

auxins Auxins are plant **hormones** found in the tips of growing shoots and rots. The hormones control the growth of the plant.

background radiation We are surrounded by radioactive materials, in rocks, in the air we breathe and particles from outer space. All these sources of radioactive particles are called background radiation.

base Bases are metal hydroxides, oxides and carbonates. Bases that dissolve in water are called **alkalis**.

capillary A capillary is a thin-walled narrow blood vessel.

carbohydrates Carbohydrates are foods made of carbon, hydrogen and oxygen. They are eaten to supply energy.

carbon cycle The carbon cycle shows how the carbon that all living things need for growth is recycled via the carbon dioxide in the atmosphere.

carnivore A carnivore is an animal which eats other animals.

catalyst A catalyst changes the rate of a chemical reaction without being changed by the reaction.

cell All living things are made of cells, which are the smallest units of living matter. All cells have a **nucleus**, **cytoplasm** and a surface membrane.

chlorophyll Chlorophyll causes the green colour found in plants which is necessary for **photosynthesis**.

chloroplast Plant cells contain chloroplasts which contain the **chlorophyll** and carry out photosynthesis.

chromosome The **nucleus of cells** contain pairs of chromosomes which contain many **genes**.

cloning Cloning is a process of making an identical copy of a living thing.

combustion Combustion is the reaction of a substance which is burned in oxygen. Combustion is an **oxidation** reaction.

compound When elements join together to form compounds they do so by forming bonds.

concentration The concentration of a solution tells us how much of a substance is dissolved in water. Concentration is measured in moles per litre or moles per dm³. The higher the concentration, the more particles of the substance are present.

condensation In condensation molecules in a vapour return to a liquid, losing energy as they do so.

conductor An electrical conductor is a material which allows an **electrical current** to pass easily. It has a low **resistance**. A thermal conductor is a material that allows thermal energy to be transferred through it easily.

cornea The cornea is the transparent outer coating of the eye.

coulomb Electric charge is measured in **coulombs** (C).

covalent bond A covalent bond between atoms forms when atoms share electrons to achieve a full **outer shell** of electrons.

cracking Cracking is the process in which a large molecule is broken into smaller molecules using a **catalyst**.

critical angle The critical angle is the **angle of incidence** which results in waves being refracted through 90°.

cytoplasm Cytoplasm is the living contents of the **cell** where the chemical processes take place.

decomposition Decomposition is a reaction in which substances are broken down, by heat, by electrolysis or by a **catalyst**.

diffraction Diffraction of waves happens when waves pass through a gap which is comparable in size to the **wavelength** of the wave.

diffusion Diffusion is the effect of randomly moving particles in a liquid or gas gradually spreading from an area of high **concentration** to an area of low concentration.

digestion During digestion food passes through the gut and is broken down into small enough molecules to pass into the blood. Food that is not digested passes out of the anus as solid waste.

digital signal A digital signal carries information as a series of 1s and 0s which code the values of the original signal.

diode A diode is an electrical component that only allows **electric current** to pass in one direction.

direct current Direct current (d.c.) always flows in the same direction.

distillation Distillation is the separation of a mixture into one or more components by **evaporation** and **condensation** of the components with the lower boiling points.

DNA DNA is the chemical which makes **chromosomes**.

effector An effector is the part of the body which responds to a stimulus, such as a muscle or gland.

efficiency Efficiency is a measure of how effectively energy is transferred in a system.

electric charge An **electron** carries a negative charge, a **proton** carries positive charge. Electric charges attract and repel each other. Electric charge is measured in **coulombs** (C).

electric current An electric current is a flow of **electric charge** around a circuit. Electric current is measured in **amps** (A).

electrolysis When an **electric current** passes through a solution or molten solid it is called electrolysis.

electrolyte An electrolyte is the liquid which conducts an **electric current** during **electrolysis**. It contains ions which carry the current.

electromagnetic induction When a conducting wire moves relative to a **magnetic field**, a **voltage** is induced across the wire. This process is called electromagnetic induction.

electromagnetic spectrum The electromagnetic spectrum is a family of waves which all travel at the same speed in a vacuum.

electron An **electron** is a very small negatively charged particle found in an atom in the space surrounding the **nucleus of the atom**. The number of electrons surrounding the nucleus is the same as the number of **protons** in the nucleus in a neutral atom.

electronic configuration The electronic configuration of an atom describes the arrangement of the atoms within the energy levels or **shells** around the atom.

element All **atoms** of an element have the same **atomic number**, the same number of **protons** and **electrons** and so the same chemical properties.

enzymes Enzymes are made of **protein** molecules. They are biological **catalysts**, molecules become temporarily attached to the enzyme during biological processes.

epicentre The epicentre of an earthquake is the place in the earth that the earthquake occurred. Seismic waves spread out from the epicentre.

equilibrium If the rate of the forward reaction and the rate of the back reaction in a **reversible reaction** are equal the reaction is in equilibrium.

evaporation Molecules near the surface of a liquid may leave the liquid to become a vapour – this is called evaporation.

exhalation Exhalation (expiration) is the process of decreasing the space inside the chest so that air pressure rises and air flows out of the lungs.

food chain A food chain shows the feeding relationship between living things and the way energy and nutrients flow through the system.

food pyramid A food pyramid gives information about the numbers of the different living organisms in a **food chain**.

food web A food web shows how **food chains** are interlinked and how organisms in an ecosystem depend on each other.

fossil fuel Fossil fuels have been created over millions of years by the decay and compression of living things, particularly plants.

fractional distillation In fractional **distillation** a mixture of several substances, such as crude oil is distilled, and the evaporated components are collected as they condense at different temperatures.

frequency Frequency is the number of waves produced each second. Frequency is measured in Hertz (Hz).

fusion During nuclear fusion two small atomic nuclei collide together with such energy that they fuse, releasing energy as electromagnetic waves.

galaxy A galaxy is a collection of many stars held together by **gravity**.

gene A **gene** is a short length of DNA which is the code for a protein. There are many genes within each **chromosome**.

genetic engineering The process of genetic engineering involves taking genes from one living thing and inserting them into the DNA of another living thing to change its characteristics.

giant lattice **Compounds** formed by **ionic bonds** form a giant structure in a lattice.

giant structure Sometimes **covalent bonds** produce giant structures which are very strong.

glucose Glucose is a simple carbohydrate produced by plants during photosynthesis. Some glucose is used as an energy source by the plant, the rest is converted to starch and stored in the leaves.

gravitational potential energy When an object is lifted against the pull of **gravity**, energy is transferred to the gravitational field. This energy is gravitational potential energy.

gravity Gravity is the force which pulls objects to the ground. Gravitational attraction acts between any two objects with mass. The strength of the gravitational field is measured in newtons / kilogram (N/kg).

groups The groups of elements in the **periodic table** are the elements which have the same number of electrons in their outer **shells** and so have similar chemical properties. A group of elements all lie in the same column in the periodic table.

half-life Half-life is the time it takes for half a quantity of radioactive material to decay to a new substance.

halogens The halogens are the elements in group VII of the **periodic table**. They have seven electrons in the outer **shell**.

herbivore A herbivore is an animal which only eats plant material.

hertz Frequency is measured in hertz (Hz). 1 Hertz = 1 per second.

hormone Hormones are chemicals which help to co-ordinate life processes.

hydrocarbons Hydrocarbons are a group of **compounds** which contain the elements hydrogen and carbon. Many hydrocarbons are derived from oil.

igneous rock Igneous rocks are formed when molten rock cools.

inhalation Inhalation (inspiration) is the process of increasing the space inside the chest so that the air pressure drops and air flows in to the lungs.

inherited disease An inherited disease is

a disease passed on from one generation to the next from the **genes** of the parents to the child.

insulator An electrical insulator is a material which does not allow an **electrical current** to pass. It has a very high **resistance**. A thermal insulator is a material that does not allow thermal energy to be transferred through it easily.

insulin Insulin is a **hormone** involved in the control of sugar levels in blood.

ion Atoms can lose or gain electrons. When they lose an electron they become a **positive ion**. When they gain an electron they become a **negative ion**.

ionic bond An ionic bond forms between two atoms when an electron is transferred from one atom to the other, forming a positive-negative **ion** pair.

iris The iris is opaque tissue which controls the size of the pupil and so controls the amount of light which can pass into the eye.

isotope **Atoms** of the same **element** that have different numbers of neutrons are called isotopes.

joule Energy is measured in joules.

kidney The kidney is the organ which controls water balance and salt balance and the **pH** of the blood. Kidneys excrete urea, hormones and medicines in the urine they produce.

kinetic energy When an object is given an **acceleration** energy is transferred to the object. This energy of a moving object is kinetic energy.

LDR An LDR (light-dependent resistor) is a component whose **resistance** value is dependent on the level of light falling on the component.

longitudinal wave A longitudinal wave is a wave whose oscillations are in the same direction as the energy is travelling.

magnetic field A magnetic field is the region in space around a magnet in which other magnets are affected.

mass The mass of an object is a measure of the amount of material in an object. Mass is measured in kilograms (kg).

mass number The mass number (A) of an **element** is the number of **protons** plus the number of **neutrons** in the **nucleus of the atom**.

meiosis Meiosis happens when a parent cell divides to create four new sex cells, each with a different combination of **chromosomes**.

metamorphic rocks Metamorphic rocks are formed when rocks are changed by heat or pressure.

microbe Microbes are small single cell organisms such as bacteria.

mitosis Mitosis is the process of cell division which results in two identical cells.

monomer A monomer is a simple molecule.

motor neurone A motor neurone is a nerve cell which transmits a signal from the spinal cord to the **effector**.

mutation A mutation is a spontaneous change in a **gene** or **chromosome** which may result in a change in the cells characterised by that gene.

negative ion A negative **ion** (anion) is formed when an atom gains an electron to achieve a full outer shell of electrons.

nephron The nephron is the structure within the **kidney** which filters out waste from the blood and allows useful materials to be reabsorbed.

neutralisation Neutralisation is the reaction between an **acid** and a **base** to produce salts and water.

neutron A neutron is a small uncharged particle, with the same mass as a proton, found in the nucleus of the atom.

newton Force is measured in newtons (N). 1 newton is the unbalanced force needed to give a **mass** of 1 kg an **acceleration** of 1 m/s^2.

nitrogen cycle All living things need nitrogen to make **proteins**. The nitrogen cycle shows how nitrogen is recycled so it is available to both plants and animals.

noble gases The noble gases are the elements in group 0/group VIII of the **periodic table**. They have a full outer shell of electrons and so are unreactive.

normal The normal is a line perpendicular to the surface at the point where a wave crosses the surface.

nucleus of a cell The nucleus of the cell is made of genetic material such as DNA. The nucleus contains the instructions for the cell.

nucleus of an atom An **atom** has a small dense positively charged nucleus where most of the **mass** is concentrated, containing **protons** and **neutrons**.

oestrogen Oestrogen is one of the sex **hormones** in females which causes puberty.

ohm Electrical **resistance** is measured in ohms (W).

optic nerve Nerve fibres from the light-sensitive cells on the **retina** form the optic nerve which passes from the eye to the brain.

optical fibres Optical fibres are very fine threads of glass through which light can pass, even when the fibre is curved around a corner.

ore An ore is a rock containing a mineral which can be extracted from the rock.

osmosis Osmosis is a special case of **diffusion** – a solvent passes through a membrane from a weak to a stronger solution. The **membrane** does not allow the passage of the solute.

oxidation An oxidation reaction is one in which oxygen combines with a substance; or a reaction where electrons are removed or a reaction where hydrogen is removed from a substance.

oxygen debt During vigorous exercise **anaerobic respiration** takes place in muscle tissue. Lactate is produced in the absence of oxygen. When exercise stops oxygen is used to respire the lactate.

periodic table The periodic table lists the **elements** in order of **atomic number**. The table is arranged into rows called **periods** and columns called **groups**.

periods The periods of elements in the **periodic table** are the elements in which the same outer **shell** is being filled up. A period of elements in the periodic table all lie in the same row.

pH The pH scale is a measure of how **acid** or **alkali** a solution is. The pH scale runs from 1 to 14.

photosynthesis Plants process water and carbon dioxide to produce **glucose** by the process of photosynthesis.

plasma Plasma is the yellow liquid part of blood which contains many dissolved substances.

polymer A polymer is a large molecule formed from many monomers by **polymerisation**.

polymerisation Polymerisation is the reaction in which many identical **monomers** are joined together to make a **polymer**.

positive ion A positive **ion** (cation) is formed when an atom loses an electron to achieve a full outer shell of electrons.

power Power is the rate at which energy is transferred in a system. Power is measured in **watts** (W) and kilowatts (kW). 1 W = 1000 kW.

progesterone Progesterone is one of the sex **hormones** which causes puberty in females.

proteins Proteins are foods made from carbon, hydrogen and nitrogen. Proteins are used to build **enzymes** and **cytoplasm**.

proton A proton is a small positive particle found in the **nucleus** of the atom.

pupil The pupil is the hole through which light passes into the eye.

radioactive decay Radioactive decay is a random process in which the **nucleus** of an atom becomes more stable by losing particles and energy.

reactivity series The Reactivity Series is a list of metals in order of decreasing reactivity. Any metal will displace a metal below it in the Reactivity Series from its solution.

receptor A receptor is a part of the body which detects a stimulus.

red blood cells Red blood cells contain haemoglobin which transports oxygen to cells of the body and returns carbon dioxide to the lungs.

redox reaction **Oxidation** and **reduction** always take place together. The combined reaction is called a redox reaction.

reduction A reduction reaction is one in which oxygen is removed from a substance; or a reaction where electrons are gained or a reaction where hydrogen is gained by a substance.

reflection Reflection of waves happens when the waves bounce off a surface.

refraction Refraction of waves happens when waves change direction due to a change in speed.

resistance Resistance of a wire is a measure of how difficult it is for an electric current to pass. Resistance is measured in **ohms** (W).

respiration Respiration is the process which transfers energy from food to the organism.

retina The retina is a light-sensitive layer at the back of the eye.

reversible reaction Reversible reactions are chemical reactions which can go both ways. The direction of the reaction depends on the condition of the reactants.

satellite A satellite is a body in orbit around a planet. Moons are natural satellites. there are many man-made satellites in orbit around the Earth.

saturated compounds In saturated compounds the atoms are joined together by single bonds.

sedimentary rocks Sedimentary rocks are formed when rock fragments are deposited and then pressed together.

seismic waves Seismic waves carry energy away from an earthquake.

sensory neurone A sensory neurone is a nerve cell which carries a signal from the **receptor**.

shells of atoms **Electrons** are grouped within an **atom** in regions of space called shells or energy levels.

Solar system The solar system is the Sun, nine planets, the asteroid belt and a number of comets.

speed Speed tells us the rate at which something moves. Speed is measured in metres / second (m/s).

stomata Stomata are pores (openings) in the surface of the leaf, through which transpiration occurs.

temperature regulation The body controls its internal temperature by varying blood flow, sweating and shivering.

terminal velocity When an object moves through a fluid there is resistance to its motion. The faster it travels the greater the resistance. When the driving force is balanced by the resistive forces the object is moving at a maximum speed called its terminal velocity.

testosterone Testosterone is the sex **hormone** which causes puberty in males.

thermistor A thermistor is an electrical component whose **resistance** changes with temperature.

total internal reflection Total internal reflection of a wave occurs when the **angle of incidence** is greater than the **critical angle**.

transformer A transformer is a pair of coils of wire linked by a piece of iron. A changing current in one coil creates a changing magnetic field in the iron which causes a changing voltage in the other coil by **electromagnetic induction**.

transition metals The transition metals are the **group** of elements in the periodic table between Group II and Group III.

transpiration Transpiration is the loss of water from a plant by evaporation from **stomata**.

transverse wave A transverse wave has the oscillations at right angles to the direction in which the energy is travelling.

unsaturated compounds In an unsaturated compound one or more of the bonds between atoms are double bonds.

vein A vein is a blood vessel with a thinner wall, with a larger space and lower pressure than an artery.

velocity Velocity tells us the **speed** of a moving object and the direction in which it is moving.

villi The surface of the small intestine is lined with villi, small 'fingers' of gut which increase the surface area for **digestion**.

volt Electrical potential difference (**voltage**) is measured in volts. 1 volt = 1 joule / coulomb.

voltage Voltage (potential difference) between two points in a circuit measures the difference in energy carried by the **electric charge** passing through the circuit. Voltage is measured in **volts** (V).

watt **Power** is measured in watts (W). 1 watt is 1 joule / second.

wavelength Wavelength is the distance from the crest of one wave to the crest of the next wave.

weight The weight of an object is the force of **gravity** on the object. Weight is measured in **newtons** (N).

white blood cells White blood cells fight infection. They make antibodies and overcome bacteria.

work Work is done when a force moves an object. When work is done energy is transferred. Work is measured in **joules**. When a force of one newton acts through one metre in the direction of the force, 1 joule of work is done.

Index